THE RED-HEADED LEAGUE

AND OTHER MYSTERY PLAYS

D1037844

SCHOLASTIC INC.

Editor: Katherine Robinson
Contributing Editor: Fran Claro
Editorial Director: Eleanor Angeles
Art Director and Designer: Marijka Kostiw

ISBN 0-590-34551-6

12 11 10 9 8 7 6   3 4 5/9

Printed in the U.S.A.   28

CONTENTS

VICTORIA'S HOUSE

a stage play by Fred Carmichael

CHARACTERS

NEIL BANNISTER, a handsome man in his 40's
VICTORIA BANNISTER, 28, a wealthy woman, recently married to Neil
MRS. CASE, the housekeeper
WINNIE, the maid
STEPHENS, the handyman and coachman
MARGARET ST. JAMES, 65, a woman who believes in the unknown
WILLIAM SCOTT, a young lawyer
CHARLES AXTON, an unexplained visitor
JANE LEIGHTON, 22, Victoria's niece

ACT ONE, SCENE ONE

The living room of a large house in England. It is the early 1900's. There is a gas heater in the fireplace. French windows lead out to the garden. A doorway leads to the rest of the house. Mrs. Case brings in a pot of coffee. She is followed by William and Margaret, two guests.

MARGARET: I remember the parties that old Frank Leighton used to have in this house, William. Wonderful food. I haven't eaten like that since. *(She notices Mrs. Case.)* Not that this meal wasn't delicious, Mrs. Case.

MRS. CASE: Thank you, Miss St. James.

MARGARET: William, I must be getting old. I find myself living in the past.

WILLIAM: You're only as old as you feel.

MARGARET: Then bury me quickly.

(They laugh.)

WILLIAM: You look very healthy to me.

MARGARET *(whispering)*: I look better than Victoria, anyway. She looks worse than she did last week.

(Neil and Victoria enter.)

NEIL *(to Victoria)*: My dear, you're getting stronger every day.

VICTORIA: I *am* feeling much better this evening. Mrs. Case, the coffee, please.

MRS. CASE: Yes, madam.

MARGARET: Victoria, it's so nice to be a guest in this house again. It's like the old times, when your father was alive.

VICTORIA: Neil, did you know that Margaret is an expert on old houses?

WILLIAM: And ghosts!

MARGARET: If you're interested, Neil, I'll give you some articles on the subject.

NEIL: Thank you. I'd like that.

VICTORIA *(to Neil):* Do you believe in ghosts?

NEIL: I don't know. Things happen that we don't understand. Call them ghosts, if you like.

MARGARET: Good for you. Another person on my side.

MRS. CASE: Excuse me, Mrs. Bannister. Perhaps I'll go get your bed ready. You might wish to retire early.

VICTORIA: Not tonight. I feel wonderful.

NEIL: A good idea, Mrs. Case. Get the room ready.

MRS. CASE: Yes, sir. *(She goes upstairs.)*

VICTORIA *(to Neil)*: I'm surprised you're willing to believe in ghosts. But then I know so little about you, even after three happy months of marriage.

NEIL: You'll be even happier when you get well.

MARGARET: What does the doctor say?

NEIL: It's a strange illness. Probably something she got in France. If I'd had *my* way, we would have taken our wedding trip right here in England.

VICTORIA: But it was *your* idea to go abroad.

NEIL *(after a pause)*: Only because I had to check on some business.

WILLIAM: What kind of business are you in?

NEIL: Importing. *(He changes the subject.)* Victoria, you've let your coffee get cold.

VICTORIA: It's all right.

MARGARET: Well, Neil, it's nice to have you here. Just think, Victoria. If I hadn't talked you into going on that vacation, you never would have met him. *(She gets up.)* William, it's time for this old body to get some rest.

WILLIAM: I think I'm being taken home.

MARGARET: You are. It's my carriage. *(She, William, and Neil exit. We hear Margaret's voice offstage.)* Neil, we must get together. I'll show you my articles about old houses and the spirits in them.

NEIL *(offstage):* We have a date then. Good night. *(He comes back to Victoria.)* Thank heaven that's over.

VICTORIA: Didn't you like them?

NEIL: Of course, but I want to be alone with you.

VICTORIA: Tomorrow I think I'll take a long walk along the cliffs.

NEIL: I don't want you to get faint and fall over the edge. Those cliffs are dangerous.

VICTORIA: Not when you've grown up here. We can take a walk together.

NEIL: I have business to take care of.

VICTORIA: Neil, what *is* this business of yours?

NEIL: You're too pretty to worry your head about it.

VICTORIA: Love has made you blind. I am *not* pretty.

NEIL: To me you're beautiful. *(He kisses her.)*

VICTORIA: Neil, the servants!

NEIL: No one is watching.

VICTORIA: Not even Mrs. Case? She's an odd one. Why did you hire her in London? There are plenty of good housekeepers here in town.

NEIL: It's not wise to hire someone from nearby. They gossip about you. Now, I think you'd better go to bed. You've had a busy evening.

VICTORIA: Not yet. I'll play the piano for you. My favorite tune. You've never heard me play before.

NEIL: I'll have Mrs. Case bring you your medicine.

VICTORIA: I don't need it tonight. I feel much better.

NEIL: That's why you need it. I want to keep you feeling better.

VICTORIA: All right. *(She goes into the music room.)*

NEIL *(calling):* Mrs. Case, a glass of water, please!

(The piano is heard. Mrs. Case brings in a glass of water.)

MRS. CASE: Here you are, sir.

(Neil adds some medicine from the desk. Then he adds some powder from an envelope he takes from his pocket.)

NEIL: Take this in to her.

MRS. CASE: Why don't you?

NEIL: I said, "Take this in to her!"

MRS. CASE: Don't you order me around. Ask me like the gentleman you're supposed to be. Then I'll take your medicine to her.

NEIL: Please, Mrs. Case.

MRS. CASE: That's better.

(She goes. Suddenly, we hear very strange music. Neil looks uneasy. The music seems to come from the house itself. Or is it Neil's imagination? The music stops. Mrs. Case is heard from the music room.)

MRS. CASE: Here's your medicine, Mrs. Bannister.

10

SCENE TWO

The next morning. Mrs. Case is winding the clock above the fireplace. Stephens enters.

STEPHENS: The carriage is out front.

MRS. CASE: Have you seen Mr. Bannister?

STEPHENS: No, but we better get started.

NEIL *(entering, angry):* There you are, Stephens. I thought you cleaned the stables every morning.

STEPHENS: I do, sir.

NEIL: I've just been down there. That's not my idea of clean stables.

STEPHENS: I never had any complaints from Mr. Leighton.

NEIL: I'm the master now. I want those stables cleaned properly.

STEPHENS: But I should drive Mrs. Case—

NEIL: I'll drive her to the station.

STEPHENS: Yes, sir. *(He exits.)*

NEIL: I had to find some excuse to keep him busy.

MRS. CASE: Good. You can't afford to make a mistake.

NEIL: I didn't before, did I?

MRS. CASE: No, but I think this one is much smarter than Mrs. Masterson.

NEIL: Quiet! I've told you not to say her name.

MRS. CASE: I remember her coming home ill after her wedding trip.

NEIL *(grabs her arm):* I swear, I'll—

MRS. CASE: Let go of me! We're partners, remember?

NEIL *(letting go):* You've got to be more careful.

MRS. CASE: So do you, losing your temper like that. I've seen you out of your mind. All those days and nights I took care of you when you stayed at my boarding house.

NEIL: It was fever.

MRS. CASE: No, that wasn't fever. I thought they'd have to take you away.

11

NEIL: All right! You'll get what's coming to you. Is your bag packed?

MRS. CASE: I'm all set. Give me the papers.

NEIL *(giving her an envelope):* Here's everything to give to Mr. Carter.

MRS. CASE: For the money you're giving him, he would kill his own mother.

NEIL: On the 10th of the month, he'll leave for Paris. He'll stay at the Hotel Royal under my name, until the 13th. When he leaves the hotel, he gives them the forwarding address of his next hotel.

MRS. CASE: Where will his next hotel be?

NEIL: In Switzerland. But he won't go there. I'll check into the Swiss hotel on the 14th. After one night, I'll leave. I'll be out of touch with everyone for the next 10 days or so.

MRS. CASE: So you couldn't possibly have been here on the 12th.

NEIL: Right. Neil Bannister was in Paris from the 10th till the 13th. Then he was in Switzerland—and other countries—on business.

MRS. CASE: So I won't see you till afterward—except for the 12th.

NEIL: Correct. *(Pause.)* I wish you could do it all yourself.

MRS. CASE: No, you're the expert.

VICTORIA *(coming downstairs):* Neil.

NEIL: Why aren't you in bed?

VICTORIA: I'm tired of being in bed.

NEIL: All right, if you feel up to it. Mrs. Case, get your bag. I'll be with you in a minute.

(Mrs. Case exits. Neil helps Victoria to a chair.)

VICTORIA: Where are you going with Mrs. Case?

NEIL: To the station. Her sister in London is ill.

VICTORIA: I kept imagining things all night. Strange voices were talking to me.

NEIL: That's from Margaret's talk about ghosts last night.

VICTORIA: I felt so strong last night. Now I feel so weak. I'm sorry I'm so ill.

NEIL: It's not your fault. It *does* make things difficult, though. I wouldn't think of leaving you now.

VICTORIA: Just to take Mrs. Case to the station?

NEIL: No, my business trip. To France and Switzerland. I was supposed to go to Paris on the 10th. But I can't leave you now.

VICTORIA: I'll be fine. Promise me you'll go.

NEIL: Well, since you put it that way. *(He takes her in his arms.)* What did I ever do to deserve you?

VICTORIA: I'm the lucky one.

MRS. CASE *(entering):* Excuse me, sir. We'd best be leaving.

NEIL *(to Victoria):* I won't be long, dear. Come along, Mrs. Case.

(They exit. Victoria feels faint.)

VICTORIA: My medicine. *(She goes to the desk. She sees a man, Axton, outside the French windows, which open like doors.)* Oh!

AXTON *(coming inside):* Hope I didn't frighten you.

VICTORIA: What do you want?

AXTON: Perhaps you've heard of me—Charles Axton, the writer.

VICTORIA: No.

AXTON: My subject is ghosts, and I'm looking for new material. Today I went to see Margaret St. James. She wasn't home, but I talked with the maid. It seems that Miss St. James is interested in this house. So I took a room at the hotel. Then I walked up here. This is a wonderful place.

VICTORIA: I'm afraid there's nothing unusual about this house.

AXTON: I remember a house just like this one. The

13

woman died. She took her own life. I was sure she would come back and haunt the place. Maybe it would turn out she was murdered. But nothing happened.

VICTORIA: You must have been disappointed.

AXTON: It was so much like this house. Poor woman. She had been ill for so long. She got weaker and weaker. Then she killed herself.

VICTORIA: How terrible.

AXTON: She had just come back from her wedding trip.

VICTORIA: How strange.

AXTON: Why?

VICTORIA: How long had she been married?

AXTON: Three months.

VICTORIA: You said she might have been murdered.

AXTON: I have a friend in the police force. He told me about it. No one knew anything about the man she married. He disappeared right after the funeral. He must have married her for her money. But she had been spending so much, there was nothing left. The police thought he might have been drugging her. But then she poisoned herself. They couldn't prove a thing.

VICTORIA: What was the woman's name?

AXTON: Leora Masterson.

VICTORIA: I don't know why you came here, Mr. Axton. But I know it wasn't to look at the house.

AXTON: Very well. I am Sergeant Axton of the London Police.

VICTORIA: Why didn't you tell me before?

AXTON: I didn't know you, Mrs. Bannister. I heard you were ill. I couldn't just come here and tell you that you're in danger.

VICTORIA: But I'm not.

AXTON: The story I told you about Leora Masterson is true. They called it suicide. The case was closed.

14

Then last week, while on vacation here, I saw a man on the street. He reminded me of someone. I wrote to headquarters. They sent me a photograph. The man is Mr. Masterson—and your husband.

VICTORIA: I don't believe it. It's a lie!

AXTON: It's not a lie that Mr. Masterson hired a housekeeper who also disappeared. A Mrs. Ethel Case. *(He takes a photo from his pocket.)* Here's the photograph of Mr. and Mrs. Masterson.

VICTORIA *(looking at it):* It's Neil. *(She almost faints. He helps her to the sofa.)*

AXTON: Is there anything I can get for you?

VICTORIA *(pointing at the desk):* My medicine.

AXTON *(getting the medicine):* What is it?

VICTORIA: I'm not sure. A doctor gave it to me in France. Neil has bought more of it.

AXTON *(tasting some):* It seems to be harmless.

VICTORIA: Of course it is. *(She takes some.)* That's strange. It doesn't taste the way it does when Neil mixes it for me.

AXTON: Perhaps he adds something else. *(He looks out the window.)* He's coming up the drive. Where can I hide?

VICTORIA *(after a pause):* Go down that way to the music room. After he's come in, you can go out the front way. I don't know what to say, Mr. Axton. It can't be true that—

AXTON: But it can.

VICTORIA: How can I know?

AXTON: Think of some way to test him. *(He goes out to the music room.)*

(Neil comes in through the French windows.)

NEIL: It's a lovely day. Perhaps you can take a walk this afternoon.

VICTORIA: Perhaps.

NEIL: It's time for your medicine.

VICTORIA: I just took it. It tasted strange, Neil.

NEIL: It must be getting old. I'll get a fresh bottle. Then we can sit outside before lunch. The fresh air will do you good. Then you won't have any more nightmares.

VICTORIA *(getting an idea):* I remembered what those voices in my dream were saying. They kept saying a woman's name over and over. It was Leora Masterson.

NEIL *(surprised):* Where did you hear that name?

VICTORIA: The voices in my dream. But I don't know any Leora Masterson.

NEIL: I don't, either.

VICTORIA: Do you think Margaret is right about old houses? Are there spirits who speak?

NEIL: Of course not. Now, let me get you some fresh medicine. *(He goes upstairs.)*

VICTORIA *(to herself):* What if it's true?

AXTON *(returning):* Well?

VICTORIA: Did you hear?

AXTON: Yes.

VICTORIA: I think he knew her. But you could be wrong. You have no proof.

AXTON: There's nothing I can arrest him for. But if I went to London, I'd probably find something in the police records. I can't leave you alone here, though.

VICTORIA: He's going away for two weeks. Even if you're right, he can't have any plans before then. So there's time to prove you're wrong.

AXTON: Or right. If you want to reach me, send a note to the hotel here. I'll be back on the 13th at the latest.

VICTORIA: Go now. Hurry.

AXTON: You've got spirit, Mrs. Bannister.

VICTORIA: I have to know for myself.

AXTON: I understand. *(He exits.)*
   (Neil comes downstairs).

NEIL: Here's a new bottle of medicine. *(He smiles.)*

17

SCENE THREE

The evening of the 12th. It is a cold, windy night. The gas fire is on in the fireplace. Victoria has finished eating from a tray. Mrs. Case enters and picks up the tray.

VICTORIA: See how my appetite has come back?

MRS. CASE: That's because you've been resting since Mr. Bannister left.

VICTORIA: I hope he's having better weather in Paris.

MRS. CASE: The wind is terrible, isn't it?

VICTORIA: Do storms scare you, Mrs. Case?

MRS. CASE: In this place, they do.

VICTORIA: You don't like this house, do you? I've never known any other home. That must be why I think it's talking to me in my dreams. I hear the rooms talking to me, but I don't understand what they mean. *(Mrs. Case starts to leave.)* They keep saying the name Leora Masterson.

MRS. CASE *(stops):* What?

VICTORIA: Leora Masterson.

MRS. CASE: What did he tell you? What do you know?

VICTORIA: Who was she?

MRS. CASE: I don't know.

(She exits. Victoria goes to the desk and writes a note to Axton. She hides it, as Mrs. Case returns.)

VICTORIA: Would you ask Winnie to come here?

MRS. CASE: Didn't I tell you? I gave her the night off. She went to her home. Is there anything I can do?

VICTORIA: No, thank you. We're alone then, aren't we?

MRS. CASE: Yes, madam.

(She exits. Victoria burns her note in the fireplace. Neil comes in through the French windows. Victoria screams in surprise.)

VICTORIA: Oh, Neil. You frightened me.

NEIL: There's nothing to be afraid of.

VICTORIA: Why aren't you in Paris?

NEIL: I didn't have to go, after all. So I rushed home to you.

MRS. CASE *(entering):* I heard a scream. Why, you've come back, Mr. Bannister.

NEIL: I'm afraid I frightened my wife.

MRS. CASE: She was just saying we are all alone here. Winnie is spending the night with her people.

NEIL: And Stephens?

MRS. CASE: He's asleep above the stables.

NEIL: I'm sorry I upset you, Victoria. You should take some sleeping powder. It will help you to get a good night's sleep.

VICTORIA: No, I'll be all right. I feel fine now.

NEIL: Mrs. Case, a glass of water, please.

MRS. CASE: Yes, sir. *(She exits.)*

(Neil turns off the gas in the fireplace.)

VICTORIA: It's cold, Neil. Leave the gas on.

NEIL: You're going right to bed.

MRS. CASE *(entering with a glass of water):* Here, Mr. Bannister.

NEIL *(taking an envelope from his pocket):* I picked this up in London. It will put you to sleep in no time.

VICTORIA: I won't take it.

NEIL: This isn't like you. You've always done what I've said.

VICTORIA: Not this time.

MRS. CASE: She's been acting very strange. She asked me if I know Leora Masterson.

NEIL: Did she? *(He pours the sleeping powder into the glass of water.)*

VICTORIA: This house kept saying the name.

NEIL: Where did you hear that name, Victoria?

VICTORIA *(crying):* The house, I tell you!

NEIL: All right. Now, drink this up.

VICTORIA: No, please!

20

NEIL *(holding the glass to her mouth):* Drink!

VICTORIA: No! Please, no!

(He forces her to drink.)

NEIL: There, now. That wasn't so bad, was it?

VICTORIA: Are you happy now?

MRS. CASE *(starting to leave with the glass):* I'll go rinse this out.

NEIL: Stay here, Mrs. Case. I can't do everything alone.

MRS. CASE: Yes, you can, sir. It was your idea.

NEIL: You're part of this.

MRS. CASE: No, sir. I merely did what you told me. I brought a glass of water. *(She exits.)*

VICTORIA: Neil, please. Get a doctor . . . before. . . .

NEIL: It's cold in here, isn't it? We better turn the gas on.

VICTORIA *(realizing what he is going to do):* No!

NEIL: Yes. *(He turns the gas on without lighting it. We hear it hissing.)* There we are.

VICTORIA *(falling asleep on the sofa):* You . . . have to . . . light it.

NEIL: Oh, I forgot. You light it, Victoria.

VICTORIA *(almost asleep):* No . . . I'm . . . too. . . .

NEIL: Then I'll help you. *(He lifts her up. Then he puts her on the floor in front of the fireplace.)* Try to turn it off. Here. Here's the handle. *(He puts her hand on the handle.)* You're too weak, aren't you? Poor Victoria. Your illness has made you so weak.

VICTORIA: Is this . . . how . . . Leora Masterson . . . ?

NEIL: You know nothing about her! Nothing! *(He starts coughing from the gas. She does, too.)* The house told you nothing about Leora Masterson! *(He starts to go out the French windows. He hears the strange music again.)* No! *(He runs out.)*

(Victoria makes a weak move to turn off the gas. She is choking. Then she is still. We hear the gas hissing.)

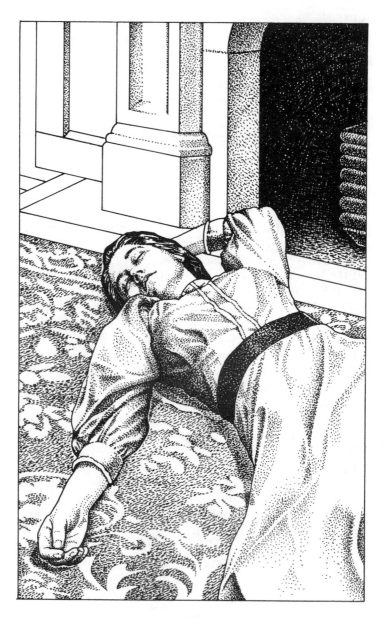

22

ACT TWO, SCENE ONE

Evening, two weeks later. Jane and William are sitting in the living room.

WILLIAM: I should have kept a closer eye on your aunt, Miss Leighton.

JANE: You must not blame yourself, Mr. Scott.

WILLIAM: It seems so impossible. And it was just when she was putting up a good fight to get well again.

JANE: That's why I won't believe that Aunt Victoria killed herself. It must have been an accident.

WILLIAM: It could have been.

JANE: Tell me about Uncle Neil. I'm looking forward to meeting him.

WILLIAM: It's strange that he didn't leave a forwarding address at the hotel in Switzerland.

JANE: It's lucky he wrote to us later from France. Otherwise, he still wouldn't know about Victoria's death. How awful for him to learn that his wife is dead and the funeral is over.

WILLIAM: You handled everything very well.

JANE: It was the least I could do. Aunt Victoria was the last of my family.

(The doorbell rings. We hear Mrs. Case's voice offstage.)

MRS. CASE *(offstage):* Mr. Bannister!

NEIL *(offstage):* Good evening, Mrs. Case. *(He enters.)* Hello, William. This must be my niece, Jane.

JANE: Yes, Uncle Neil.

NEIL: I'm sorry we have to meet at such a sad time.

JANE: Uncle Neil—

NEIL: Please. No sympathy. We must go on with our lives. Victoria would have wished us to. *(The doorbell rings.)* Are we expecting anyone?

JANE: No.

MRS. CASE *(entering):* A Mr. Axton is here, sir.

NEIL: Tell him I'm not up to seeing anyone.

AXTON *(entering):* Forgive my coming so late. I just got in town, and I heard the sad news. *(He turns to William.)* Mr. Bannister?

WILLIAM: No.

NEIL: I'm Neil Bannister.

AXTON: I'm Charles Axton. I was a good friend of Victoria's father.
(Mrs. Case exits.)

NEIL: This is Miss Jane Leighton, my wife's niece.

AXTON: How do you do?

NEIL: And William Scott, the family lawyer.

WILLIAM: Not too good a lawyer, I'm afraid. You'll see, Neil, when we have a chance to talk business.

NEIL: What business?

WILLIAM: Some papers I should have given to Victoria to sign.

NEIL: What papers?

WILLIAM: We can discuss it later.

NEIL *(louder):* What papers?

WILLIAM: Victoria's will. Before she was married, everything was left to Jane, as the only relative.

NEIL: And now?

WILLIAM: I drew up a new will for Victoria. It was never signed. We will have to go to court. As her husband, you should get your share.

NEIL: I thought everything was taken care of!

WILLIAM: Since Victoria was so ill, I didn't want to bother her. *(He turns to Axton.)* Please forgive us for talking business.

NEIL: Yes, I'm sorry. I'm very upset tonight.

AXTON: I understand. It was stupid of me to come this evening. I'll be going now.

WILLIAM: Let me drive you into town.

AXTON: Thank you. Mr. Bannister, my sympathy. Perhaps we can get together in a few days.

NEIL: Thank you for coming. Jane, would you see them to the door, please?

(Jane, Axton, and William exit. Mrs. Case enters.)

MRS. CASE: Did everything go all right? Was Carter in Paris?

NEIL: Yes.

MRS. CASE: You saw him?

NEIL: For a minute. That's all it took.

MRS. CASE: What do you mean? You didn't—

NEIL: Now we don't have to worry about his talking.

MRS. CASE: You're going too far.

NEIL: Don't worry.

MRS. CASE: Strange things have been happening here. The bell in her room keeps ringing.

NEIL: Victoria's room?

MRS. CASE: Yes. But when I get there, the room's always empty. And one night, I heard the piano.

NEIL: It must have been Jane.

MRS. CASE: No, she was in bed. I heard that tune Mrs. Bannister used to play.

NEIL: You imagined it.

(Jane enters. Mrs. Case exits.)

NEIL: Jane, will you do me a favor? Victoria used to play the piano. Will you play something for me?

JANE: I wish I could. But I never learned.

NEIL: I see.

JANE *(starting to go):* You must be tired. We'll have a long talk in the morning.

NEIL: I hope you will stay here for a while.

JANE: I'd like that. It's lonely in London.

NEIL: You're all alone?

JANE: Yes, since my parents died.

NEIL: Good night, Jane.

(She goes upstairs. Neil starts turning out the lights. He hears piano music from the music room. As he starts toward the music room, the music stops. He looks around wildly, then goes upstairs. Suddenly, we see Victoria outside the French windows. She is dressed the way she was when she was killed.)

SCENE TWO

The next evening. Jane and Neil are in the living room. Jane is looking out the French windows.

JANE: The moonlight is so bright. It makes the bushes look silver.

NEIL: I prefer sunlight. It leaves nothing to the imagination.

JANE: I like to imagine things.

NEIL: Not me. I have no imagination.

JANE: Yes, you do. This morning you asked me if I heard the piano last night. You were sure I must have heard it. Mrs. Case imagines things, too. She asked me if I rang the bell in Aunt Victoria's room.

NEIL: Well, you did, didn't you?

JANE: Of course not.

NEIL: Mrs. Case must be upset, like the rest of us.

JANE *(seeing something in the garden)*: How strange. It isn't windy, but those bushes moved. It looked like someone moving around.

NEIL *(looking out)*: Where?

JANE: Beyond the tree. There it is again. Like a dress.

NEIL: I don't see anything.

JANE: It must have been a trick of the moonlight.
(The piano music is heard.)

NEIL: Jane, do you hear anything?

JANE: No.
(He starts toward the music room. The music stops.)

NEIL: It doesn't matter.

JANE: I think I'll go up to bed now.

NEIL: Good night.
(She exits. Neil pulls the bell rope. Winnie enters.)

WINNIE: Yes, Mr. Bannister.

NEIL: Did you fix Miss Leighton's room for the night?

WINNIE: Yes, sir.

NEIL: Winnie, did you enjoy my piano playing just now? I'm trying to learn my wife's favorite tune.

27

WINNIE: I didn't hear you, sir.

NEIL *(angry):* You're lying!

WINNIE: Why would I lie about a thing like that, sir?

NEIL: Never mind. You can go to bed now.

WINNIE: Yes, sir. *(The doorbell rings.)* I'll get it, sir. *(She exits. We hear her voice from offstage.)* Miss St. James.

MARGARET *(offstage):* Mr. Bannister is expecting me. *(She enters.)* There you are, Neil.

NEIL: I wasn't sure you'd come.

MARGARET: After the note you sent, nothing could have kept me away. Have you seen anything?

NEIL: I don't know. Mrs. Case keeps hearing the bell in my wife's room. I've heard the piano playing when no one is around. It's always the same tune—Victoria's favorite. Tonight Jane thought she saw someone walking in the garden. And before Victoria died, she kept telling me the house was saying things to her. Is it possible that Victoria is still here?

MARGARET: It's possible.

NEIL: But why?

MARGARET: There must be something she left unfinished. You must know what it is.

NEIL: No. There's nothing I can think of.

MARGARET: Then I'll have to study up on it. There may be other cases like this one. I'll go right home and get to work.

NEIL: Stephens will drive you. Thank you for coming.

MARGARET: Good night, Neil. *(She exits.)*

(Mrs. Case enters.)

MRS. CASE: I'm leaving tomorrow.

NEIL: You can't. I can't stay in this house alone.

MRS. CASE: You're frightened. If you go on like this, you'll have a breakdown. You'll be worse off than when I found you. No, I'm leaving tomorrow. And I'm taking my share of the money.

NEIL: You know I haven't gotten the money yet.

MRS. CASE: You've got some you can spare. Send the rest to me later . . . something every month.

NEIL: Every month? That wasn't our agreement.

MRS. CASE: Our agreement has changed, starting now.

NEIL: Do you think I'll let you get away with this?

MRS. CASE: What choice do you have? *(She turns her back, to warm her hands at the fireplace. She doesn't see Neil take a cord from the curtains.)* I haven't the strength to face this house anymore. I don't believe in ghosts. But there's *something* here.

NEIL: I know.

MRS. CASE: So I'm getting out.

NEIL: So you can live off me the rest of your life?

MRS. CASE: That's it.

(He goes up behind her, lifting the cord to strangle her. Then he sees Victoria outside the windows. He drops the cord.)

NEIL: Look. Look there!

MRS. CASE: She's back. She's come back!

(Victoria points her finger at Neil. Mrs. Case screams and runs out of the room. Neil stands there, frozen.)

SCENE THREE

The next evening. Jane, Neil, William, and Axton are in the living room.

WILLIAM: The people in town are making up wilder and wilder stories every hour.

AXTON: The waitress at the hotel told me this house is evil.

JANE: Do they really believe a house can be good or bad?

WILLIAM: Yes, even though it was just an accident.

JANE: It *is* strange. Aunt Victoria died just two weeks ago. And now poor Mrs. Case.

AXTON: What was it that made Mrs. Case fall off the cliff last night? And what made her scream?

JANE: Something must have scared her, so she ran out of the house.

NEIL: It must have been a prowler. Remember, Jane, you thought you saw someone in the garden.

AXTON: Anyway, the police are sure it was an accident.

WILLIAM: Well, come along, Mr. Axton. It's time for us to go.

NEIL: I'll be visiting you soon, William. We have Victoria's will to clear up.

WILLIAM: Of course, Neil.

(William and Axton exit. Winnie enters.)

WINNIE: Mr. Bannister, I'm going to my parents' house. I'll be back in the morning.

NEIL: But this isn't your night off.

WINNIE: I know, sir. But I'm scared. When I'm in my room, I have a feeling I'm not alone.

NEIL: You can't go off alone at this time of night.

WINNIE: I'll feel safer out there than in here. I'll be back in the morning. *(She exits.)*

NEIL: Well, we're alone, Jane, aren't we?

JANE: Yes, Uncle. This morning, I took some flowers to

Aunt Victoria's grave. I noticed something odd. The flowers I left there yesterday had been stepped on.

NEIL *(nervously):* It must have been Stephens.

JANE: He wouldn't walk on the flowers.

NEIL *(shouting):* It must have been Stephens!

JANE: You seem very upset tonight. Can I get you some sleeping powder?

NEIL: No.

JANE: Then I'm going to bed.

NEIL: Good night. I'll turn off the gas. *(She goes. He turns off the gas in the fireplace. But then it makes the hissing sound it made before Victoria was killed.)* I shut it off. I know I shut if off! *(He turns it off again. He turns out the lights. The room is dark, except for moonlight from the windows. Victoria's tune is heard on the piano. Neil rushes toward the music room. The music stops. He turns and opens the French windows.)* Victoria, are you there? *(Jane screams from upstairs. He rushes toward the stairs.)* Jane!

JANE *(running downstairs):* I heard it!

NEIL: What?

JANE: A voice. It kept saying, "Leora Masterson. Victoria Bannister. Leora Masterson."

NEIL: You must have imagined it!

JANE: No, I heard it. Why would someone be calling Aunt Victoria? And who is Leora Masterson?
(Neil looks around the house. Then he speaks as if under a spell.)

NEIL: She's just someone I used to know.

JANE: Who was she?

NEIL: A woman—a lonely woman.

JANE: Did she die, too?

NEIL: Yes.

JANE: The way Aunt Victoria died?

NEIL: Yes. Now they're together—acting together.

JANE: What do you mean?

31

NEIL: They want to destroy me. *(Suddenly, he sees Victoria at the top of the stairs.)* Victoria.

JANE: What about her, Uncle?

NEIL: Don't you see her?

JANE: No.

NEIL *(grabbing her by the shoulders)*: You must see her! Don't lie to me! *(He pushes her aside. Then he looks up at Victoria.)* So you've come back, Victoria. Both of you? But why? What do you want? *(Victoria points her finger at him.)* Me? No, you can't get me. Neither of you. I killed both of you. You and Leora. I killed you, and you can't do a thing to me!

(Axton and William enter.)

AXTON: Thank you, Mr. Bannister. That's all we wanted to hear.

(Victoria goes away.)

NEIL: What? Who—?

AXTON: Just Mr. Scott and myself.

NEIL *(trying to seem calm)*: William, you won't believe me, but I thought I saw something. But it wasn't true. *(He points at the stairs.)* You don't see anything, do you?

WILLIAM: No.

NEIL: Do you, Mr. Axton?

AXTON: Sergeant Axton, sir, of the London Police. You're under arrest for the murder of Mrs. Leora Masterson. Mr. Scott, turn on the lights, please.

NEIL: Leora? I don't know any Leora Masterson. That's just a voice . . . a voice in the house.

AXTON: That's not true, sir. She was your wife.

JANE: He said he killed her.

AXTON: We were listening. I've been waiting for this, Mr. Bannister or Masterson—or whatever your real name is. I knew you were planning to murder your second wife.

NEIL: You couldn't have. You would have stopped me.

AXTON: But I did, Mr. Bannister.

(Victoria comes downstairs.)

NEIL: Victoria!

VICTORIA: Yes, Neil. I'm alive.

NEIL: How can you be?

AXTON: You were almost successful, Mr. Bannister. I thought she would be safe while you were away. Then I realized that might be part of your plan. So I stayed close to the house. I came in as soon as you left her lying there. Luckily, I was just in time.

NEIL: But she was buried. There was a funeral.

AXTON: The casket was empty. That was easy to arrange with the local police. We had Winnie pretend to find your wife's body. We let Mrs. Case have only a quick look. Mrs. Bannister acted her part very well. Tonight I told Mr. Scott about our plan. He can serve as witness to your confession.

NEIL: But why did you go through all this? Victoria could have testified that I tried to kill her.

AXTON: That was only attempted murder. I wanted you for the real murder of Leora Masterson. And tonight we heard your confession.

VICTORIA: Please take him away from here.

AXTON *(to Neil):* Shall we go?

NEIL: But Jane heard the voices, too.

AXTON: I told her what to do.

NEIL: The piano?

AXTON: That was your wife, of course. Ever since you tried to murder her, we've planned every step.

NEIL: You couldn't have. The gas went on by itself.

AXTON: What gas?

NEIL: In the fireplace. I heard it hissing. I smelled it. *(Suddenly, we hear the strange music, which seems to come from the house itself.)* This house is alive! It makes sounds. Don't you hear them?

AXTON: What are you talking about?

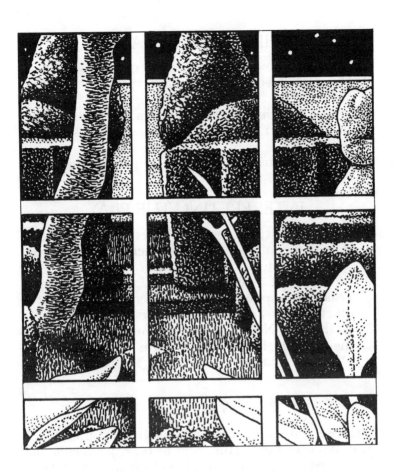

NEIL *(to the others):* You hear them, don't you? Don't you? What is it? Help me! *(He sinks into a chair.)*
VICTORIA *(to Axton):* What is it?
AXTON: I don't know, Mrs. Bannister. Perhaps Margaret St. James is right. There may be things we will never understand.

THE END

CHECKING THE FACTS

1. Who was Leora Masterson? How did she die?
2. How does Neil make it appear that Victoria kills herself?
3. When Neil thinks Victoria is dead, he hears tunes that she used to play on the piano. Who is playing these tunes?
4. How is Neil tricked into confessing to murder?

INTERPRETING THE PLAY

1. Why does Victoria become ill after she marries Neil? When Axton gives Victoria her medicine, why doesn't it taste the same as usual?
2. What sort of deal have Neil and Mrs. Case made? What sort of power does each seem to have over the other? How—and why—does Mrs. Case die?
3. At the end, Neil hears strange music. Do you think the house really *is* haunted? Or is the music only in Neil's imagination?

WRITING

Suppose you are Victoria and Neil has just tried to kill you. Write a letter to Jane, your niece. Explain what has happened and why you want her to visit for a while.

THE CASE OF
THE BERYL CORONET

a Sherlock Holmes mystery by Sir Arthur Conan Doyle

CHARACTERS

SHERLOCK HOLMES, the famous English detective
DR. JOHN WATSON, his friend and assistant
ALEXANDER BENSON, a banker
ARTHUR BENSON, his son
MARY BENSON, Arthur's stepcousin
SIR GEORGE BURNWELL, Arthur's friend
NOBLEMAN, a famous Englishman
MAID, who works for Sir George Burnwell

SCENE ONE

Holmes's sitting room. It is a cold February day. Snow is on the ground. Holmes is poking the fire in the fireplace. Watson is looking out the window.

WATSON: Holmes, there is a madman rushing down the street. He is waving his hands around, and his head is swinging from side to side.

HOLMES *(looking out the window):* I believe he is coming here.

WATSON: Here?

HOLMES: Yes, to ask me for help.

(The doorbell rings. Watson answers the door. A gentleman follows him into the room.)

BENSON *(gasping for breath):* I am . . . I am . . . .

HOLMES *(pointing to a chair):* You are tired from running. Wait until you have caught your breath.

BENSON *(sitting):* You must think I am crazy.

HOLMES: I think you have had some great trouble.

BENSON: It is terrible!

HOLMES: Calm yourself, sir. Tell me who you are and what has happened to you.

BENSON: I am Alexander Benson, an owner of the Benson and Stevenson Bank.

WATSON: That is one of the largest banks in England.

38

BENSON: Yes. We make much of our money by giving loans. To get loans, people must leave us some property as security. If the loan is not paid, we keep the property. People usually use silverware or small pieces of jewelry as security. So I was amazed by the offer I got yesterday. I was in my office at the bank. A famous nobleman came in. You would recognize his name, but I must keep it a secret.

SCENE TWO

Benson's office—the day before. A clerk brings in a noble-man. Then the clerk leaves.

BENSON *(with great respect):* Good morning, my lord.

NOBLEMAN: Mr. Benson, I wish to borrow some money.

BENSON: Yes, my lord.

NOBLEMAN: I must have 100,000 pounds at once. I could borrow it from friends. But I would rather make this a business deal. I do not want anyone but you to know about it.

BENSON: How long do you want the money?

NOBLEMAN: Until next Monday. Then I will repay the loan—plus interest.

BENSON: I certainly trust you, my lord. But I must be fair to my partner. I must insist that you leave something for security.

NOBLEMAN: Of course. *(He hands a jewelry case to Benson.)* Have you heard of the beryl coronet?

BENSON: Oh, yes! It is one of the most valuable treasures in England. *(He gasps as he opens the case.)*

NOBLEMAN: There are 39 large beryls in that crown. The gems and the gold around them are priceless. The coronet is worth much more than 100,000 pounds. But I will leave it with you as security. Do you question its worth?

BENSON: Oh, no! But—

NOBLEMAN: You wonder why I would leave such a treasure with you? Well, you have a fine reputation. I trust you not to tell anyone about our business here today. And I trust you not to let anything happen to the coronet. No beryls in the world can match those you are holding. I will be back for the coronet in four days. Now, may I have the 100,000 pounds?

BENSON: Yes, my lord.

40

SCENE THREE

Holmes's sitting room. Benson continues his story.

BENSON: I locked the coronet in my office safe. When evening came, I did not dare to leave it in the office. I decided to take it home with me each night. I wanted it nearby at all times. When I got home, I locked it in a drawer in my dressing room.

HOLMES: Who lives in your house?

BENSON: Two maids and a butler have worked for me for several years. Another maid, Lucy Parr, joined the staff recently. She is a good worker. I have only one complaint about her. She is pretty, and young men hang around to talk to her.

HOLMES: Do you have a family?

BENSON: Yes. My dear wife died 20 years ago. I have one child, Arthur. I wish I could say I am proud of him, but I am not. I spoiled him. When my wife died, he was all I had to love. I gave him whatever he wanted.

HOLMES: What does he do?

BENSON: I hoped he would take over my business, but he is not interested in it. He is wild. It started when he joined a club. He made friends with young men who have plenty of money and bad habits. He kept losing money by gambling. He tried to break away from these people. But his friend Sir George Burnwell drew him back again.

HOLMES: What is Sir George Burnwell like?

BENSON: He has been to my home often. He is very clever and charming. I can see why Arthur is influenced by him. But there is something about him that I don't trust. I believe that Mary agrees with me.

WATSON: Who is Mary?

BENSON: My stepniece. Her father—my stepbrother— died five years ago. I adopted her then. She is a lovely young woman. She has disappointed me only once.

HOLMES: What was that about?

BENSON: Arthur asked her to marry him. He loves her, but she turned him down. I think she might have changed his bad ways. But now it is too late!

WATSON: What do you mean?

BENSON: You will soon find out. Last night I told Mary and Arthur about the coronet. We were in the sitting room, having coffee after dinner.

SCENE FOUR

Benson's sitting room—the evening before. Mary, Arthur, and Benson are seated. Lucy Parr is collecting their coffee cups.

ARTHUR: Where are you keeping the coronet?

BENSON: In my dresser.

ARTHUR: I hope we do not have any burglars tonight.

BENSON: It is locked up.

ARTHUR: Any old key will fit that lock. When I was a child, I opened it myself. I used the key for the kitchen cupboard.

(Lucy Parr leaves with the coffee cups.)

BENSON: But no one knows that the coronet is there. Still, to be safe, I am going upstairs now. Good night, Mary. Good night, Arthur. *(He goes upstairs. Arthur follows him into Benson's dressing room.)*

ARTHUR: Father, will you let me have 200 pounds?

BENSON: No! I have already given you too much money.

ARTHUR: You have been very kind. But if I don't have this money, I will not be able to go to the club again.

BENSON: That is good news!

ARTHUR: But I would be disgraced. I must pay back

my debts. If you will not give me the money, I must get it another way. *(He leaves.)*

(Benson unlocks the dresser. The coronet is still there. He locks it up again. Then he walks around the house, checking windows and doors. Downstairs he sees Mary locking a window in the hall.)

MARY: Uncle, did you say Lucy could go out tonight?

BENSON: No.

MARY: She came in the back door a minute ago. I guess she only went to the gate to speak to someone. But I do not think it is safe.

BENSON: I will speak to her about it in the morning. Are all the windows and doors locked?

MARY: Yes.

BENSON: Then I will say good night again. *(He goes upstairs.)*

SCENE FIVE

Benson's bedroom—several hours later. He is asleep. The sound of a window slamming shut wakes him up. Soon he hears footsteps. He gets up and enters his dressing room. There is Arthur, holding the coronet. He is not wearing a jacket, and his feet are bare.

BENSON: Arthur, you thief! *(Arthur drops the coronet in surprise. Benson picks it up. He sees that part of the crown is missing.)* You have ruined it! Three of the gems are missing! Where are they?

ARTHUR: No gems are missing from it. They cannot be missing!

BENSON: So, you are a liar as well as a thief!

ARTHUR *(angry):* You have called me enough names. I will not stand it any longer. I will leave this house tomorrow—and never come back.

BENSON: You will leave this house with the police! *(A maid has heard the argument. She enters. Benson turns to her.)* Run and get the police!
(She leaves.)

ARTHUR: Are you really going to charge me with theft?

BENSON: Yes. This is not just an argument between a father and a son. The coronet belongs to a very important person. Now it is ruined! And so is my reputation!

ARTHUR: Before the police arrive, please let me leave the house for five minutes. It will help us both.

BENSON: What? And let you run away? Or hide what you have stolen? No! Just tell me what you have done with the missing gems. Then I will forgive you.

ARTHUR: Keep your forgiveness for those who ask you for it!
(Mary enters. When she sees the coronet and Arthur's face, she faints.)

SCENE SIX

Holmes's sitting room. Benson continues his story.

BENSON: The police searched Arthur's room. They did not find anything. Arthur is now in jail. The police are puzzled by the case. You must help me! I have lost my honor, the gems, and my son—all in one night!

HOLMES: Do you have many visitors?

BENSON: No. My partner and his family sometimes visit. Now and then Arthur's friends visit. Sir George Burnwell has been over several times lately.

HOLMES: Do you go out often?

BENSON: Arthur does. Mary and I do not care to go out.

HOLMES: That is strange for a young woman.

BENSON: Mary is shy.

HOLMES: This matter seems to have shocked her very much.

BENSON: Yes. She seems even more upset that I am.

HOLMES: Are you sure your son is guilty?

BENSON: Of course. He had the coronet in his hand.

HOLMES: I do not think that is proof.

BENSON: But what was he doing there? If he is innocent, why did he not say so?

HOLMES: But if he is guilty, why did he not lie? His silence seems to tell us two things. He is guilty—and not guilty. What did the police think of the noise that woke you?

BENSON: They think it was Arthur closing his bedroom door.

HOLMES: Nonsense. Would a thief slam a door and wake up everyone? What did the police say about the missing gems?

BENSON: They are still searching the house.

HOLMES: Have they looked outside the house?

BENSON: Yes. They searched the whole garden.

HOLMES: You seem to think your son found the coronet and broke off three of the gems. You seem to think he went off and hid them. You seem to think he then came back with the other 36 gems. Do you really believe he would do that—at the risk of being caught by you?

BENSON: What else can I believe? If he is innocent, why doesn't he say so?

HOLMES: It is our job to find out. We will go to your home with you.

(Benson rises and goes into the hall.)

WATSON: I have faith in you, Holmes. But I do not see how Arthur Benson can be innocent.

HOLMES: We shall see.

SCENE SEVEN

Benson's sitting room. Benson and Watson are sitting by a fireplace.

BENSON: Mr. Holmes has been looking around outside for a long time.

WATSON: He does not like to miss any possible clues.

(Mary enters. She is pale. Her eyes are red from crying. She goes to Benson.)

MARY: Uncle, have you told the police to set Arthur free?

BENSON: No. The police are still working on the case.

MARY: I am sure that Arthur is innocent.

BENSON: Why is he silent if he is innocent?

MARY: Maybe he is angry that you suspect him.

BENSON: Of course I suspect him. He was holding the coronet.

MARY: I am sure he was only looking at it. Please let the matter drop.

BENSON: I will not let it drop until the gems are found. In fact, I have brought a detective here to study the case.

47

MARY *(looking at Watson):* Is this the gentleman?

BENSON: No, this is his friend, Dr. Watson. Mr. Holmes is looking around outside.

MARY: What can he hope to find there? *(Holmes enters. Mary turns to him.)* I hope, sir, that you will prove that Arthur is innocent.

HOLMES: I believe you are Miss Mary Benson. May I ask you a question or two?

MARY: Of course.

HOLMES: Did you hear anything last night?

MARY: Not until my uncle began talking loudly.

HOLMES: Had you locked all the windows and doors?

MARY: Yes.

HOLMES: One of the maids has a sweetheart. You told your uncle she had been out to see him. Is that right?

MARY: Yes. She served our coffee in the sitting room last night. She may have heard Uncle talking about the coronet.

HOLMES: Do you think she and her sweetheart planned the burglary?

BENSON: What is the good of this talk? I saw Arthur with the coronet in his hand!

HOLMES: We will come back to that, sir. *(He turns to Mary.)* Did you see this maid come in through the back door?

MARY: Yes. I went to lock it. I met her as she was coming in. I saw the man outside.

HOLMES: Do you know him?

MARY: Yes. He delivers our vegetables.

HOLMES: Did he stand on the left side of the door?

MARY: Yes, he did.

HOLMES: Does he have a wooden leg?

MARY *(surprised):* How do you know that?

HOLMES *(ignoring her question):* I want to look at the windows on this floor. *(He goes from window to window. He stops at one and studies the sill.)* Now I will go upstairs. *(They all go up to Benson's dressing room. Holmes sees a key on top of the dresser.)* Is this the key that opened the dresser?

BENSON: Yes. It is the key my son spoke about. It is the key for the kitchen cupboard.

HOLMES *(opening the dresser drawer with the key):* The lock makes no noise, so it did not wake you. *(He takes out the jewelry case and opens it. He studies the coronet.)*

WATSON: Those are the finest beryls I have ever seen.

HOLMES: Mr. Benson, you can see where the missing gems were. Please break off the piece next to it.

BENSON *(shocked):* I would never do such a thing!

HOLMES: Then I will try. *(He tries, but the coronet does not break.)* My fingers are very strong. But I cannot break this by myself. It would take the strength of two people.

BENSON *(after a pause):* I do not know what to think.

HOLMES: You said your son was barefoot when you saw him. Is that right?

BENSON: Yes.

HOLMES: I am having good luck with this case. Now, it is time for me to go home.

BENSON: But where are the gems?

HOLMES: I cannot tell.

BENSON: Well, at least tell me what happened here last night.

HOLMES: Visit me tomorrow morning. Then I will make things clearer. First, I want to get the gems back. What are you willing to pay for them?

BENSON: My entire fortune!

HOLMES: I will see you tomorrow. Good-bye. *(He and Watson leave.)*

50

SCENE EIGHT

Holmes's sitting room—later that day. Watson is reading. Holmes enters, dressed as a beggar. He is carrying an old boot, which he throws in a corner. Then he pours himself some tea.

WATSON: What is up?

HOLMES: I am going to the other side of town. I may be gone for quite a while.

WATSON: Where have you been in that beggar's disguise?

HOLMES: Several places. I have been outside Benson's house again. But I must not waste time talking. I must get out of these clothes and become myself again. *(He goes upstairs.)*

SCENE NINE

The same scene—the next morning. Watson and Holmes are there. The doorbell rings.

WATSON: Perhaps that is Mr. Benson. *(He answers the door. Then he brings Mr. Benson into the room.)* Mr. Benson, you look more upset than you did yesterday.

BENSON *(sitting):* What have I done to deserve all this trouble? Two days ago, I was happy. Now I face a lonely and disgraced old age. My last hope of happiness—Mary—has left me.

WATSON: Left you?

BENSON: Yes. Last night, I told her she should have married Arthur. Then he would have turned out all right. That is why she wrote this note. *(He takes a note from his pocket and reads it aloud.)* "Dearest Uncle, I feel I have brought great trouble to you. If I had acted differently, you might still be happy. I feel I must leave you forever. Do not worry about my future. And do not search for me. You will

51

never find me. In life or in death, I am your loving Mary." Mr. Holmes, do you think she plans to kill herself?

HOLMES: No. But I believe that some of your troubles are over.

BENSON: What have you learned? Where are the gems?

HOLMES: Is 3,000 pounds too much to ask for them?

BENSON: I would pay 30,000 pounds!

HOLMES: Well, 3,000 pounds will do. And I suppose a reward of 1,000 pounds for me would be fair. *(Benson nods. Holmes hands him a pen.)* Please write out a check for 4,000 pounds.

(Benson takes out his checkbook. He writes out a check and gives it to Holmes. Holmes reaches into his pocket. He takes out the broken piece of the coronet and gives it to Benson.)

BENSON *(very happy):* You have it! I am saved!

HOLMES: There is one other thing you owe.

BENSON *(picking up the pen):* Name the amount, and I will pay it.

HOLMES: You owe nothing more to me. You owe an apology to your son. He has acted in a way that should make a father proud.

BENSON: You mean he did not take the gems?

HOLMES: I have been telling you that.

BENSON: I must go to him at once. I must tell him that you know the truth.

HOLMES: He knows already. I spoke to him. Since he would not tell me the story, I told it to him. He had to admit it was true.

BENSON: What *is* the true story?

HOLMES: I will tell you. But first you should know that Mary and Sir George Burnwell have eloped.

BENSON: Impossible!

HOLMES: You and your son did not know Sir George very well. He is a heartless villain. He flattered

Mary. She thought he really loved her. She began seeing him almost every evening.

BENSON: I do not believe it!

HOLMES: I will tell you what happened on the night of the crime. Remember when you found Mary locking a window? She had just been talking to Sir George through that window.

SCENE TEN

Benson's home—the night of the crime. Mary is facing a hall window on the first floor. The window is open. Sir George is standing outside in the snow.

SIR GEORGE: I would do anything for you, Mary. I want you to be my wife. But I must have some money. That is why you must get the coronet for me. If you love me, do as I have told you.

MARY: Sh! I hear my uncle coming downstairs. *(She closes the window and locks it. Benson appears.)* Uncle, did you say Lucy could go out tonight?

SCENE ELEVEN

Holmes's sitting room. Benson looks shocked.

BENSON: I remember! Mary! How could she?

HOLMES: Later that night, Arthur had a hard time going to sleep. When he heard footsteps in the hall, he got up. He saw Mary enter your dressing room. He quickly put on a shirt and trousers. Before he could put on some shoes, Mary went downstairs with the coronet. Arthur followed her quietly and hid behind a drape. He saw Mary give the coronet to Sir George through the window.

BENSON: Why didn't he stop her?

HOLMES: Because he loved her. He did not want her to get into trouble. But when she went upstairs, he knew he must do something—for your sake. He jumped through the window and ran after Sir George. When he caught him, he grabbed the coronet. The two men struggled for it. Arthur hit Sir George, cutting him over one eye. Suddenly, there was the sound of metal snapping. Arthur found the coronet in his hand and ran back to the house with it. He closed the window and took the coronet to your dressing room. He did not realize that part of it had been broken off.

BENSON: That was when I found him. Poor boy.

HOLMES: You made him angry by calling him names. He would not explain what had happened—to protect Mary.

BENSON: That is why she fainted when she saw the coronet. What a fool I have been!

WATSON: Now I see why Arthur wanted to go outside for five minutes. He wanted to go to where the struggle had taken place. He hoped to find the missing gems.

HOLMES: Exactly.

BENSON: Mr. Holmes, how did you figure all this out?

HOLMES: I searched outside your house. No snow had fallen since the night before. I knew that footprints in the snow would help me. I could see that a man with a wooden leg had stood near the back door. A woman had come out to talk to him, then gone back inside. These two must have been the maid and her sweetheart. I found other tracks on the west side of the house. The tracks of a booted man went up to and away from the hall window. On top of these were the tracks of bare feet. The booted man had walked. The barefoot man had run. I followed the tracks away from the house. I came to where a struggle must have taken place. The snow was trampled, and there were drops of blood on it.

WATSON: Sir George's blood?

HOLMES: Yes.

BENSON: How do you know the boot tracks belonged to Sir George?

HOLMES: Yesterday, I dressed as a beggar. I went to the back door of Sir George's house. I spoke with one of the maids.

SCENE TWELVE

The back door of Sir George's house—the day before. Holmes is talking to a maid.

HOLMES *(in a humble voice):* Miss, I don't mean to bother you. But a poor fellow like myself needs some boots in this weather. Does your master have an old pair that he doesn't need anymore?

MAID: I'm not sure. Sir Burnwell went out a while ago. He went to his doctor. He got a bad cut on his forehead last night.

HOLMES: How did it happen?

MAID: He didn't say.

HOLMES: Well, maybe you can help me. With a house like this, your master must be rich. I'm sure he wouldn't miss an old pair of boots. Any old boots will do me. And I will pay you six shillings.

MAID *(after a pause):* I'll see what I can find.

SCENE THIRTEEN

Holmes's sitting room. Watson and Benson are listening.

WATSON: So that's why you brought that old boot here. Did it fit the tracks outside Mr. Benson's house?

HOLMES: Perfectly.

BENSON: I saw a beggar near the house yesterday. So that was you!

HOLMES: Yes.

BENSON: But the gems! How did you get the gems?

HOLMES: I went home and changed my clothes. Then I paid a visit to Sir George.

SCENE FOURTEEN

Sir George's sitting room—the day before. Holmes and Sir George are standing, facing each other.

HOLMES: A valuable coronet was taken from Alexander Benson's house last night. What do you know about it?

SIR GEORGE: Why would I know anything about it?

HOLMES: You visit the Benson family often. You and Arthur Benson are friends.

SIR GEORGE: We belong to the same club. But I have not seen him recently.

HOLMES: I know that you went to the Benson house last night. You talked to Mary through a hall window. Later, she handed you the coronet through the same window.

SIR GEORGE *(taking the poker from the fireplace):* That is pure nonsense. *(Before he can hit Holmes with the poker, Holmes take out a gun.)*

HOLMES *(pointing the gun at Sir George):* Please put that poker down. *(Sir George obeys him.)* Thank you. Now, tell me where the three missing beryls are.

SIR GEORGE *(frightened):* I do not have them! I swear!

HOLMES: If this gun were to go off, it would look like self-defense. After all, you planned to kill me with that poker.

SIR GEORGE *(desperately):* I sold the gems. I did not get much for them. But I wanted to get rid of them fast. They were too hot to keep.

SCENE FIFTEEN

Holmes's sitting room. Holmes finishes his story.

HOLMES: Sir George told me the name of the man who had the gems. I visited the man. It was clear he did not know how valuable the gems were. He agreed to sell them to me for 3,000 pounds. Then I went to tell your son that everything was all right.

BENSON: I cannot thank you enough for your help. Now I must go to my son and ask him to forgive me. To think that I trusted Mary and not Arthur. I wonder where poor Mary is now.

HOLMES: I imagine she is wherever Sir George Burnwell is. And I imagine the police will catch up with them—if they haven't already.

THE END

CHECKING THE FACTS

1. Why is Mr. Benson disappointed in his son Arthur? Why does he accuse Arthur of stealing three beryls from the beryl coronet?
2. How is Lucy made to appear guilty?
3. Which two people actually try to steal the beryl coronet?
4. Who prevents the theft?

INTERPRETING THE PLAY

1. How—and why—have Mr. Benson and Mary been blind to the truth?
2. Why does Sherlock Holmes believe that Arthur is innocent? How does Arthur prove to be noble?
3. How does Sherlock Holmes make use of footprints outside Mr. Benson's house to solve the mystery?

WRITING

Suppose that Arthur and Mary run into each other five years from now. What would they say to each other? Write a brief conversation between them.

DARK POSSESSION

a teleplay by Gore Vidal

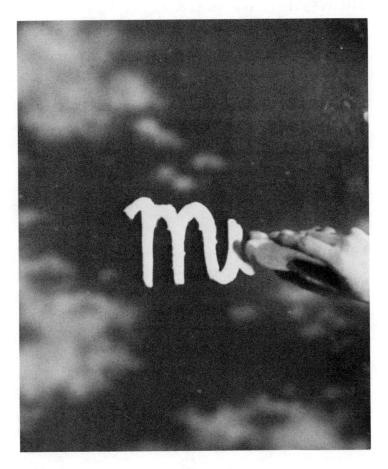

CHARACTERS

CHARLOTTE BELL WHEELER, widow of John
  Wheeler
MRS. WICKS, the housekeeper
EMILY BELL, Charlotte's older sister
ANN BELL, Charlotte's younger sister
DR. ROGER WARING, a doctor engaged to marry Ann
GENERAL BELL, father of Charlotte, Emily, and Ann
MR. WESTON, police inspector

ACT ONE

*Fade in on the living room of the Bell home in Concord,
New Hampshire. The year is 1911. Charlotte is opening
some mail at a desk. Mrs. Wicks, the housekeeper, is
standing next to her. Charlotte gasps and drops the letter
she has been reading.*

MRS. WICKS: What is it? What is the matter?
  *(Charlotte rushes from the room, passing her older sister
  Emily at the doorway.)*
EMILY: Good morning, Charlotte. I—*(She stops speaking
  as Charlotte hurries upstairs.)*
MRS. WICKS: Good morning, Miss Emily.
EMILY: What's wrong with Charlotte?
MRS. WICKS *(picking up the letter):* She got another ter-
  rible letter. This is the seventh so far.
EMILY: We must ignore them. I suppose this one
  wasn't signed, either.
MRS. WICKS: No. *(She gives the letter to Emily.)*
EMILY *(after reading it silently):* This is worse than the
  others. Listen to the last part: "Only you and I
  know what really happened to your husband,
  John. But soon others are going to find out. Soon
  even the police will know that you killed him."

MRS. WICKS *(shocked):* What a terrible thing to say!

EMILY *(picking up a picture from the desk):* I remember taking this picture of John. It was in the spring, before he married Charlotte. John and I were very happy—until Charlotte took him away from me!

MRS. WICKS *(sternly):* Emily, don't talk that way. Charlotte and John were a happy couple. Now he's dead, and Charlotte keeps getting these letters.

EMILY: Whoever is writing them knows too much about this family.

(Mrs. Wicks glares at Emily, as Emily's sister Ann enters the room.)

ANN: Good morning, Emily. We missed you at breakfast.

EMILY: I had one of my headaches.

ANN: You've been having a lot of them lately. Why don't you ask Roger to give you some medicine? He's coming over to see me this morning. I can hardly believe we're going to get married. I was beginning to feel like an old maid.

MRS. WICKS *(looking uneasily at Emily):* Nonsense. A woman isn't an old maid until she's dead.

EMILY *(to Ann):* Charlotte just got another letter. This one accuses her of killing John.

ANN: I don't believe it!

MRS. WICKS: Poor Miss Charlotte will lose her mind if we don't stop those letters. I think we should take them to the police. But Miss Charlotte says it's none of their business. People will begin to gossip, she says.

EMILY: We *can't* take the letters to the police. The letter today accuses Charlotte of murder. If the police see it, they'll want to question us.

ANN: She didn't kill John. So why should we be afraid?

MRS. WICKS: Miss Emily *does* have a point. The police might not understand things.

ANN: I think we should at least tell Father what's been going on.

MRS. WICKS: You mustn't bother the General. He's much too old for trouble now.

EMILY: He wouldn't do anything if he could. *(The doorbell rings.)* That must be Roger. I'll let him in. *(She leaves.)*

ANN *(to Mrs. Wicks):* Was Charlotte very upset by this letter?

MRS. WICKS: Yes, poor thing.

ROGER *(entering):* Good morning, Mrs. Wicks. Ann.

MRS. WICKS: Good morning, Doctor. We're expecting you tonight for dinner. Will you be here?

ROGER: I'm looking forward to it.

(Mrs. Wicks leaves.)

ANN *(upset):* Roger, you've got to help us.

ROGER: What is it?

ANN: Someone has been sending Charlotte the most awful letters. This one came today. *(She gives him the letter.)*

ROGER: Why, you can hardly read the handwriting.

ANN *(as he reads the letter):* It says terrible things about all of us, but mostly about Charlotte. We're so worried about her health. She can hardly sleep at night. Sometimes when you speak to her, she doesn't hear.

ROGER: This is quite a letter. How *did* her husband die?

ANN: He was shot in his office—with his own gun.

ROGER: Did they find who did it?

ANN: In a way. John was an assistant district attorney. He was prosecuting some blackmailers. Everyone knows that the killer was one of the gang. They had threatened to kill him.

ROGER: But was the actual murderer ever found?

ANN: No. After John's death, the gang disappeared.

ROGER: What happened to Charlotte then?

ANN: She nearly lost her mind. She was very much in love with John.

ROGER *(suddenly):* Look! There's no postmark on this envelope. The letter was never mailed!

ANN: Do you think someone brought it here, and put it in the mailbox?

ROGER: At the risk of being caught? No. I think the letter was written by someone in this house. Ann, get a sample of everyone's handwriting. Then compare them to the letters.

ANN *(nervously):* All right. I'll try.

(Cut to the dining room, that evening. The Bells and Roger are seated at the table. The General, who is in a wheelchair, looks bored.)

CHARLOTTE: Roger, you must think Concord is very quiet after living in Boston.

ROGER: Not at all. *(He looks at Ann.)* Not now.

EMILY *(sharply):* Roger is just being polite. Concord can't compare with Boston.

CHARLOTTE: Why, Emily! What a thing to say!

EMILY: John liked Boston better, too. He never liked living here.

CHARLOTTE: John? Do you mean my husband?

EMILY: Yes. When *I* was engaged to him, we talked about living in Boston. He wanted to open a law office there. *(She gets up.)* Excuse me. I'm going to get my knitting. *(She leaves.)*

GENERAL *(in a cranky tone):* Where's my coffee?

(Charlotte goes over to him and pours his coffee.)

ANN *(whispering to Roger):* I checked everyone's handwriting. No one in this house could have written those letters.

ROGER *(whispering):* Handwriting can be disguised.

CHARLOTTE *(sitting down):* Now, Father, please be friendly. We want Roger to feel welcome here.

(The General frowns. Emily comes back to the table with her knitting.)

66

GENERAL: Where's my pipe?

EMILY: Maybe you left it in the living room.

GENERAL: I'll get it myself. You can't find anything. *(He wheels himself out of the room.)*

CHARLOTTE *(trying to make everyone relax):* This winter has been so long and cold. I can't wait for spring.

EMILY: Spring and summer are boring here, too. Roger, wait until you've lived in Concord for a while. There's nothing to do but eat, sleep, talk, and write letters.

CHARLOTTE: Emily, I've never heard you talk this way before.

(The General wheels himself back into the room.)

EMILY *(bitterly):* But Boston isn't dull. If I had married John, we would have lived in Boston, and he'd be alive today.

CHARLOTTE: I don't know what you're talking about.

GENERAL *(suddenly):* It's a messy thing when two girls like the same fellow.

CHARLOTTE *(uneasy):* Father, maybe you should go to bed now.

GENERAL: I'm perfectly happy sitting up. I don't want to be rude to our guest. *(He chuckles.)*

CHARLOTTE *(standing up):* Well, I think I'll go to bed. I've had such a . . . a busy day. Good night, Roger. Visit us again soon.

ROGER: Thank you, and good night.

(Charlotte leaves.)

ANN: Emily, it wasn't very nice of you to talk to Charlotte about John.

EMILY: Well, I don't think it was very nice when—

(There is a scream from Charlotte in the hall. Everyone rushes to her. She is leaning on a table, sobbing. On the hall mirror, written in soap, is the word "Murderess." Fade out.)

ACT TWO

Fade in on the living room, the next morning. Charlotte is lying on the sofa. She looks annoyed, unlike her usual self.

MRS. WICKS *(entering with a glass of water)*: It's time for your medicine. *(Charlotte doesn't even look at her.)* I wish you'd let me open the curtains. It's so sunny outside. *(Silence.)* I'll bring you some tea when Dr. Waring comes to see you. After last night, I told Miss Emily we should go to the police. She said no. She's wrong, though. We could all be killed in our beds by strangers coming in and writing on mirrors. *(Charlotte suddenly shivers.)* It's cold in here. I'll put more wood on the fire.

(When Mrs. Wicks goes to the fireplace, Charlotte looks around slyly. She looks away quickly when Mrs. Wicks turns around.)

CHARLOTTE *(in a harsh tone)*: What do doctors carry in those black bags?

MRS. WICKS: I suppose they carry medicines.

CHARLOTTE: I wonder if they carry poison.

MRS. WICKS: You mustn't think of such things. We'll soon find out who's been sending those letters. Then it will all be over.

(The doorbell rings. Mrs. Wicks goes to answer it. As soon as she is alone, Charlotte throws the glass of water on the floor. Then she covers her face with her hands.)

ROGER *(entering)*: Charlotte?

(She uncovers her face. She no longer looks annoyed. Roger takes her pulse.)

ROGER: I know last night was a bad shock for you.

CHARLOTTE: It was worse than you know.

ROGER: Why don't you let some sun in here?

CHARLOTTE: The light hurts my eyes.

ROGER: Would you like me to talk to the General about

this? He must suspect something. He saw the mirror last night.

CHARLOTTE: No. I don't want him to read the letters.

ROGER: Then I think you should go to the police.

CHARLOTTE: You're probably right. I don't think we . . . I can wait any longer.

ROGER: Would you like me to talk to them?

CHARLOTTE: No, I think I'd better.

ROGER: Soon?

CHARLOTTE: Yes. It's not the letters I mind so much. It's the other things which keep happening.

ROGER: Like what?

CHARLOTTE: Someone is watching me and waiting. I don't know why she's watching me, but I feel it. I think I'll meet her soon, face to face. Then I'll die. You see, whoever is watching me wants to kill me.

ROGER (*surprised*): Who is it? You must suspect someone.

CHARLOTTE: Yes, but I could be wrong. I don't have any proof.

ROGER: I want to help you. Do you mind telling me about your husband's death?

CHARLOTTE: I mind very much. But I'll tell you anything you want to know.

ROGER: Was Emily really in love with John?

CHARLOTTE: I don't know. She might have loved him in her strange way. She was shy with men. I think she imagined that John loved her. I think she really believes that I stole him from her. I didn't, though.

ROGER: What did you do the day John was killed?

CHARLOTTE: There was a storm in the morning. Then I came here to have lunch with Emily and Father. Ann was away in Boston.

ROGER: What time did he die?

CHARLOTTE: Sometime in the afternoon. No one knows what time exactly. His body was found in the evening.

70

ROGER: Where were you and Emily after lunch?

CHARLOTTE: I don't remember. I really don't.

ROGER: Were you together?

CHARLOTTE: Emily says we weren't. I don't remember. I think I went a little crazy when I was told he died.

ROGER: Is there anything you'd like to do?

CHARLOTTE: You're very kind, but nothing will help. I have a feeling this will be over very soon. Something is going to happen!

ROGER: But what?

EMILY (entering): Excuse me. Roger, Father would like to talk to you upstairs.

ROGER (to Charlotte): I'll be right back. (He leaves.)

CHARLOTTE: Emily, I'm going to the police tomorrow.

EMILY: Do whatever you like.

CHARLOTTE: I can't stand any more of this.

EMILY: I'm sure you can't.

(Cut to the living room, that evening. Charlotte, Emily, and Ann are there. The doorbell rings.)

ANN: That must be Roger. (She leaves, then comes back with Roger.)

ROGER: Good evening, everyone.

CHARLOTTE: Good evening. Sit down by the fire here. You must be cold.

ROGER: Yes, it's below zero outside. By the way, are you expecting a visitor?

CHARLOTTE: No one but you.

ROGER: I thought I saw someone not far behind me. (The doorbell rings.) I'll get it. (He leaves, then comes back with Mr. Weston.) This is Mr. Weston. He works for the police department.

WESTON: I was passing by, so I thought I'd stop in, Mrs. . . . Mrs. . . . ?

CHARLOTTE: I'm Mrs. Wheeler. These are my sisters, Emily and Ann. What can we do for you?

WESTON: May I please speak with the General?

71

CHARLOTTE: I'm sorry. He's asleep.

WESTON: Well, I guess it can wait.

CHARLOTTE: I'm afraid it can't.

WESTON *(surprised)*: What do you mean?

CHARLOTTE: You got an unsigned letter, didn't you?

WESTON: Why, yes. How did you know?

CHARLOTTE: I've gotten some, too. You may read them if you like.

WESTON: We don't believe what the letter says. It's crazy. But we figured we should find out who might have sent it.

CHARLOTTE: I hope you do. I was going to see you tomorrow about the letters I've gotten.

WESTON: That's what our letter said!

CHARLOTTE *(puzzled)*: But who could have known I was going to the police? I didn't tell anyone but— *(She stops suddenly.)*

ROGER: Officer, I suggest you see Mrs. Wheeler another time. She hasn't been well, and—

CHARLOTTE: I'm all right. Did the letter say that I murdered my husband?

WESTON *(uncomfortably)*: Well, yes. It said something like that.

CHARLOTTE: The police must know it's not true.

WESTON: We do, and we want to help you.

CHARLOTTE *(looking at Emily)*: I think I know who sent those letters. I'll talk to you tomorrow, Mr. Weston. I'll have the whole story for you then.

WESTON: Good night, Mrs. Wheeler. I'll come by about 5:00 tomorrow afternoon. *(He leaves the room with Roger and Ann. When they are gone, Charlotte turns on Emily.)*

CHARLOTTE *(very upset)*: Now are you satisfied?

EMILY: What do you mean?

CHARLOTTE: I suspected you from the start. But I couldn't believe you would go this far. I couldn't believe you would accuse me of murder!

EMILY: You're out of your mind!

CHARLOTTE: No, I'm not. *You* are out of *your* mind— with hate! You were jealous of John and me. You wanted him for yourself.
(Roger and Ann come back into the room. Charlotte and Emily do not notice them.)

EMILY: You've said enough, Charlotte.

CHARLOTTE: I was a fool not to know you were in love with John. But he hardly knew you were alive.

EMILY: That's not true!

CHARLOTTE: You pretended that John loved you. You pretended that I took him away from you. But he thought you were plain-looking! He felt sorry for you!

EMILY: Stop it! You knew I loved John. You married him to spite me. You could charm men in a way I never could. But John did love me, before you started flirting with him.

CHARLOTTE: How can you say that?

EMILY: Because it's true. It's also true that you wouldn't let him go to Boston.

CHARLOTTE: That's what the unsigned letters say.

EMILY: *I* didn't write those letters. But whoever did knows what we both know.

CHARLOTTE: And what is that?

EMILY: They know that you killed your husband! Charlotte, you killed John! Don't try to deny it! *(She runs out of the room.)*

CHARLOTTE *(quietly):* I think I'll go to bed now. *(She leaves the room in a daze.)*

ANN *(to Roger):* It can't be true. Emily couldn't have said such a thing.

ROGER: And Charlotte couldn't have killed John. Or could she have?

ANN: I don't know. I don't know. I'm so confused.
(Fade out.)

ACT THREE

Fade in on the living room, the next morning. Roger is talking with General Bell.

GENERAL: I can't breathe. I'm cold all the time. This room feels like the North Pole. I'm sick, and no one cares.

ROGER: General, I've taken your temperature. I assure you that it's normal.

GENERAL *(angrily)*: I know when I'm sick, young man. I was sick before you were born.

ROGER: Yes, sir. But I would like to talk to you about Charlotte.

GENERAL: Charlotte? I thought you were marrying Ann.

ROGER: I am, but I'm worried about Charlotte.

GENERAL: I don't want to talk about her.

ROGER: Do you understand what's going on?

GENERAL: It's none of my business.

ROGER: Someone has told the police that Charlotte killed John.

GENERAL *(surprised when Roger mentions the police)*: Are you sure?

ROGER: A police inspector came here last night.

GENERAL: Jealous women cause so much trouble.

ROGER: Do you think Emily told the police?

GENERAL: Who else would tell them? She's been jealous of Charlotte all her life.

ROGER: How was John Wheeler killed?

GENERAL: Why? Do you think Charlotte killed him?

ROGER: Did Charlotte and John ever argue about leaving Concord?

GENERAL: No. She adored him. I never could see why. I think he wanted to move to Boston. Then he changed his mind. Do you feel that wind? I need some hot tea. Get Mrs. Wicks.

75

ROGER: Yes sir. *(He goes into the hall, as Emily enters the front door.)* Emily, I would like to talk to you about Charlotte.

EMILY: I'm afraid that's none of your business. Why do you keep prying into our affairs?

ROGER: I want to help. I'm Charlotte's doctor. I'm going to marry Ann.

EMILY: I'm sorry. I can't help you.

(Emily goes upstairs quickly. Roger enters the dining room. Ann is there, polishing silverware.)

ROGER: Your father wants Mrs. Wicks to take him some tea.

ANN: Is Charlotte still asleep?

ROGER: She was a half hour ago. I've been trying to talk with your father.

ANN: I suppose he wasn't much help.

ROGER: He won't take this seriously. He's more interested in his tea. Where is Mrs. Wicks?

ANN: Upstairs.

ROGER: You know, I think I'm beginning to understand what happened. I—

(They hear a scream from the second floor. They rush to the foot of the stairs. Charlotte is standing at the top of the stairs. Her hair is a mess. Her eyes are terrified. She looks over her shoulder as if someone were behind her.)

CHARLOTTE *(screaming)*: Leave me alone! Stop watching me!

(Charlotte falls downstairs, as if she has been pushed from behind. Mrs. Wicks and Emily appear and run down after her. The General wheels himself into the hall. Roger picks up Charlotte and carries her to the sofa.)

ROGER: Ann, get my bag. It's in the hall. Get some water, too.

MRS. WICKS: What happened, Doctor?

ROGER: It looked as if she were pushed down the stairs.

(Ann comes back with his bag and a glass of water.)

CHARLOTTE *(opening her eyes):* She tried to kill me. She said she would. She did the same thing before she killed John.

ROGER *(softly):* Who is she?

CHARLOTTE: She's been watching me for years. She's been waiting. Whenever I was happy, she did something to ruin it. Then she fell in love with John. But *she* couldn't have him. And she wouldn't let *me* have him. Stop her! Please stop her!

ROGER: Who, Charlotte? Who is it that should be stopped?

(Charlotte begins to twist about wildly. Roger shakes her by the shoulders. Suddenly, she is still. An odd look comes into her eyes.)

ROGER *(softly):* Who wrote those letters?

CHARLOTTE *(harshly):* I did!

(Everyone looks shocked.)

ROGER *(to Ann):* Get everyone out of here.

(Ann pushes the General's wheelchair out. Mrs. Wicks and Emily follow them.)

ROGER *(to Charlotte):* Why did you write those letters?

CHARLOTTE: To punish her.

ROGER: Who?

CHARLOTTE: Charlotte. She had everything. I had nothing. It was always that way.

ROGER: Who are *you*?

CHARLOTTE: Janet. That's just like Charlotte not to tell you. She never tells anyone my name. She's ashamed of me. *(She laughs.)*

ROGER: Have you known Charlotte for very long?

CHARLOTTE: All my life. I used to write her notes, but she never answered them. She tried to pretend I wasn't real. She shouldn't have done that.

ROGER: Were you jealous of her?

CHARLOTTE *(laughing):* No! I couldn't be jealous of such a weak person. But I hated her.

ROGER: Did you kill John Wheeler?

CHARLOTTE (*smiling*): What a silly question. (*Roger shakes her. She becomes very angry.*) She didn't deserve him. Why should she be happy? I wasn't happy. I killed him. But everyone else will think Charlotte did it.

(*Charlotte begins laughing wildly. Roger takes a hypodermic needle from his bag. He gives Charlotte a shot, which calms her down. She closes her eyes, as Ann walks in.*)

ANN: What's wrong with her? Why did she say she wrote those letters?

ROGER: Because she did write them. Part of her wrote them.

ANN: I don't understand.

GENERAL'S VOICE (*from another room*): Ann? Where are you?

ROGER (*quickly*): She's two people. You'd better go back to the others. Don't tell them what's happened.

(*Ann leaves. Charlotte opens her eyes.*)

ROGER: Charlotte?

CHARLOTTE (*sounding like herself again*): What am I doing here?

ROGER: You fell down the stairs. Don't you remember?

CHARLOTTE: No. (*Then she becomes tense.*) Yes, I do remember. Someone was behind me. I thought it was Emily. She was saying terrible things to me. Then I fell.

ROGER: It wasn't Emily.

CHARLOTTE (*confused*): Has something gone wrong with my memory?

ROGER: And Emily didn't write those letters.

CHARLOTTE: If she didn't, who did?

ROGER: You did.

CHARLOTTE: What are you saying?

ROGER: Listen to me very carefully. You are two people. It used to be called "being possessed." The new name for it is "multiple personality."

78

CHARLOTTE: What does that mean?

ROGER: A few minutes ago, you said your name was Janet. You said you hated Charlotte. You admitted writing those letters.

CHARLOTTE: I can't believe it. I know I don't remember certain things. But I could never be someone else.

ROGER: Those times you can't remember, you're Janet. I began to suspect this when you told me what happened the day John died. You remembered the morning clearly. But you couldn't remember what happened that afternoon.

CHARLOTTE *(frightened):* You mean I was someone else that afternoon?

ROGER: I think so. I think the part of yourself called Janet killed John.

CHARLOTTE: It's not true!

ROGER: I wish I could agree with you. Now, we do not have much time. Janet is starting to get control of you. You and I are going to have to fight her.
(Charlotte covers her face with her hands. Then she takes her hands away. She is smiling. She is Janet again.)

CHARLOTTE *(mocking):* Poor Charlotte. The police are coming here to get her. I've taken care of that.

ROGER: What have you done, Janet?

CHARLOTTE: Wait and see. I have a few surprises left. *(She laughs. Roger shakes her. She becomes Charlotte again and speaks softly.)* I feel so sleepy.

ROGER: I know. I gave you something to help you relax. I'm going to write to a specialist in Boston. With his help, we may be able to do something.

CHARLOTTE: What can he do for me? I killed my own husband. I can become another person without knowing it.

ROGER: We'll deal with that later. Right now, you must get some rest. I'll get Mrs. Wicks and Ann. They'll put you to bed.

80

(As soon as Roger leaves, she becomes Janet. She grins when she sees Roger's bag on a nearby table. She goes to the bag and takes out a bottle of clear liquid. She pours the liquid into the glass of water. She puts the bottle back. Then she lies down on the sofa and closes her eyes. Roger, Ann, and Mrs. Wicks enter.)

ROGER *(taking a pill from the bag):* Mrs. Wicks, give this to her when she opens her eyes.

MRS. WICKS: Miss Charlotte?

CHARLOTTE *(opening her eyes):* I feel so strange.

MRS. WICKS *(giving her the pill):* Take this, dear. Then we'll put you to bed.
(Charlotte swallows the pill, along with the liquid in the water glass. Then Mrs. Wicks helps her stand up.)

CHARLOTTE: I've become so much trouble for everyone.

ROGER: Don't worry. Just get some sleep. Then we'll have a long talk.
(Charlotte and Mrs. Wicks leave.)

ANN: What are we going to do?

ROGER: Maybe a specialist can help. If not, we'll have to declare her insane. It's the only thing we can do.
(Mrs. Wicks screams from the hall. Ann and Roger rush into the hall. Charlotte lies at the foot of the stairs. Roger examines her.)

MRS. WICKS: Doctor, what's wrong? She said that she couldn't breathe. She said something about Janet. Then she fell down.

ROGER *(examining Charlotte):* She's dead. She was poisoned. But I don't know how. *(Then he finds the empty bottle in his bag. He holds it up, frowning.)*

ANN: It was her other self, wasn't it?

ROGER: Yes.
(Fade out.)

THE END

81

CHECKING THE FACTS

1. Charlotte gets a letter accusing her of killing her husband John. Why does Roger think it was written by someone in the same house?
2. Why is Emily bitter toward Charlotte? Why does this make her seem guilty? How does General Bell's view of Emily make her seem guilty?
3. According to Roger, what is "multiple personality"?
4. Who killed John?

INTERPRETING THE PLAY

1. Emily accuses Charlotte of stealing John away from her. Charlotte accuses Emily of imagining that John loved her. What do you think is true?
2. After Charlotte falls downstairs, she says, "She tried to kill me." Who is it that Charlotte is talking about?
3. Who is Janet? Why did she kill John? Why did she write nasty, unsigned letters to Charlotte? Does Charlotte know who Janet is at first?
4. How does Charlotte die? Who causes her death?

WRITING

Suppose you are Roger and you've been asked to testify in court as to why Charlotte killed John and, later, herself. Write a short summary of what you would tell the court.

THE DEAD SLEEP LIGHTLY

a radio play by John Dickson Carr

CHARACTERS

NARRATOR
DR. GIDEON FELL, a private detective
HOSKINS, his servant
GEORGE PENDLETON, a publisher
PAMELA BENNETT, his secretary
MRS. TANCRED, his housekeeper
INSPECTOR HADLEY, a police detective
TELEPHONE OPERATOR
WOMAN'S VOICE

NARRATOR: It was very dark that night in London in 1933. Wind whistled in the narrow streets and growled in the chimneys. It even made its way into the warm study of Dr. Gideon Fell, two stories up from the street. There, before a fire, Dr. Fell sat dozing in an armchair.
(We hear several long snores. A door opens, then closes.)
HOSKINS: Dr. Fell! Wake up, sir! There's a lunatic downstairs!
DR. FELL *(yawning):* Why don't you show him up?
HOSKINS: Are you sure you want to see him sir?
DR. FELL: That depends. What kind of lunatic is he?
HOSKINS: He's a big, fine-looking man, about 50 years old. But he's shaking all over. He said his name is Pendleton.
DR FELL: I wonder if it's George Pendleton, the successful publisher. Show him in, Hoskins.
(The door bursts open.)
PENDLETON *(very upset):* Are you Dr. Gideon Fell?
DR. FELL: Yes, sir. Mr. Pendleton?
PENDLETON: Yes. I followed your man here upstairs. I hope you will excuse my barging in like this.
DR. FELL: Calm down, and sit over here by the fire. That will be all, Hoskins.

HOSKINS *(reluctantly):* Very good, sir.

(The door closes as Hoskins goes out.)

PENDLETON: Doctor, I thought I stepped on some clay soil as I was coming up the stairs just now. Was that my imagination?

DR. FELL: Clay soil?

PENDLETON: Yes, the kind that is often found in graveyards. It's on my mind, you see, because I went to a funeral yesterday.

DR. FELL: Is that why you are so upset?

PENDLETON: No. The person who died was only a member of a club I belong to. I went to the funeral because I was expected to show my respect. I'm a busy man, but it pays to keep up social duties like that.

DR. FELL: Please go on.

PENDLETON: It was a wet day in Kensal Cemetery. I was planning to leave home the next day on a long vacation. After that, I was going to sell my house and rent an apartment in the city. Pamela Bennett, my secretary, was with me at the funeral. On our way out of the cemetery, we must have lost our way, because . . . .

(Pendleton's voice fades into the sound of thunder. We hear rain falling during the following conversation. We realize the conversation took place yesterday in the cemetery, after the funeral.)

PAMELA: This looks like an old part of the cemetery.

PENDLETON: It is. It's where they bury you when you haven't much money. Take care to remember that, Miss Bennett.

PAMELA: We must have taken the wrong path, Mr. Pendleton. I'm sorry if I got the directions mixed up.

PENDLETON: Don't mention it. It's a small matter. Miss Bennett, you're the best secretary I've ever had. Why do you want to leave your job?

PAMELA: I want to get married.

PENDLETON: Who is the man, and what does he do?

PAMELA: Frank is a radio technician.

PENDLETON: Hah! I'll bet he doesn't make as much as I pay you. Why do you want to marry him? It will just interfere with your career, and . . . . No!

PAMELA: What's wrong?

PENDLETON: Do you see that grave at the end of this row? The name has almost disappeared.

PAMELA: Yes. It says, "To the Memory of Mary Ellen Kimball."

PENDLETON: Poor Mary Ellen! Now that I think about it, she had an aunt living here in Kensal.

PAMELA: Did you know her well?

PENDLETON: I'll tell you a secret, Miss Bennett. I was married to her very briefly, but . . . .

PAMELA: What, sir?

PENDLETON: It's not easy to explain. You see, I used to be poor. I had to make my way in the world, and Mary Ellen couldn't help me. I soon realized I had to get out of that marriage. I had to have a wealthy wife or none at all. I was sorry to break with her, but I had other things to think of.

PAMELA (*whispering*): You snake!

(*Her words are drowned out by thunder.*)

PENDLETON: Did you say something?

PAMELA: No. We'd better get back to the car. This wet clay soil is ruining my shoes.

PENDLETON: Of course I was sorry to hear of Mary Ellen's death.

PAMELA: You could have some flowers put on her grave. Shall I call someone to do that for you?

PENDLETON: That's a good idea. But how will they be able to find the grave?

PAMELA: Each one has a number cut into the stone at one side. This one is Kensal 1-9-3-3. It sounds like a phone number, doesn't it?

86

PENDLETON: Yes. Kensal 1-9-3-3. Kensal 1-9-3-3. *(Pause.)* Mary Ellen always said she'd come back if I called her. But it's too late for me to do anything now, isn't it?

PAMELA: It's much too late, Mr. Pendleton.

(We hear thunder. Then we hear Pendleton talking to Dr. Fell again.)

PENDLETON: That's what happened at the cemetery, Dr. Fell. Then, for some reason, I began to get nervous. I couldn't eat lunch. I couldn't get any work done at the office. That number kept running through my head. Kensal 1-9-3-3. Then, when I went home that evening, everything went wrong. First, I had lost my key, and Mrs. Tancred, my housekeeper, had to let me in. . . .

(A doorbell rings. A door opens.)

MRS. TANCRED *(surprised):* Why, sir, I didn't know it was you.

(Pendleton enters his house. The door closes.)

PENDLETON: I'm sorry to trouble you, Mrs. Tancred. I seem to have lost my key. *(Pause.)* What are my bags doing in the front hall?

MRS. TANCRED: They are packed and ready for you, sir. I hope you haven't forgotten that you're taking a vacation.

PENDLETON: Oh, yes. Of course.

MRS. TANCRED: It's a pity that you're selling the house. But it must have been lonely for you here at times.

PENDLETON *(fiercely):* I am never lonely!

MRS. TANCRED: Yes, sir.

PENDLETON: There are many people who envy me!

MRS. TANCRED: Of course, sir.

PENDLETON: I will have dinner at 7:30.

MRS. TANCRED: Yes, sir.

(We hear her footsteps leaving.)

PENDLETON *(to himself):* I can't stand the idea of having dinner alone tonight. I know! I'll call Bill Fraser, and we'll go out for dinner.

(We hear a phone receiver being lifted. Then the receiver hook is pressed up and down.)

PENDLETON: Hello? Operator?

OPERATOR: Number, please?

PENDLETON: I want. . . . What is Bill's number?

OPERATOR: Number, please?

PENDLETON *(blurting out):* Kensal 1-9-3-3. *(Thunder crashes.)* What have I said?

OPERATOR: Kensal 1-9-3-3.

PENDLETON: Operator, wait! I've made a mistake!

OPERATOR: I'm ringing Kensal 1-9-3-3, sir.

(There's a ringing tone. Then a young woman's voice answers. It is very faint.)

WOMAN'S VOICE: Hello?

PENDLETON *(wildly):* There's been a mistake!

WOMAN'S VOICE: George, dear? Is that you?

PENDLETON: Who is this?

WOMAN'S VOICE: It's Mary Ellen, dear. Don't you recognize my voice?

PENDLETON: No! No!

WOMAN'S VOICE: I knew you'd call sooner or later. Now I'll come back to you.

PENDLETON: You're not Mary Ellen! Mary Ellen is dead!

WOMAN'S VOICE: Yes, dear. But the dead sleep lightly, and they can be lonely.

PENDLETON: I won't listen to you!

WOMAN'S VOICE: I'll be there by 7:00. And don't worry. I'll wear a veil so you won't be frightened by the way I look now.

PENDLETON *(terrified):* Stay away! Do you hear?

WOMAN'S VOICE: Remember, I'll be there when the clock strikes seven times. Good-bye, dear.

(There is a click. Then Pendleton hangs up the phone.)

PENDLETON *(shouting):* Mrs. Tancred! *(We hear footsteps* *approaching.)* Who's been playing tricks on the telephone?

MRS. TANCRED: You haven't been trying to use the phone, have you?

PENDLETON: I called a friend of mine. A woman answered and pretended to be somebody I used to know.

MRS. TANCRED: Sir, the phone was disconnected this morning because you're selling the house. Don't you remember? A man came this morning to disconnect the wires.

PENDLETON: Are you mad, or am I?

MRS. TANCRED: Look for yourself. There's the cord. It's not connected to anything.

PENDLETON: You don't believe me, do you?

MRS. TANCRED: I've got to fix your dinner now, sir.
(Her footsteps start to leave.)

PENDLETON: Wait! *(The footsteps stop.)* Don't leave me! What time is it?

MRS. TANCRED: There's a clock on the mantel, sir. It must be—
(The clock strikes seven times. Music comes up and fades out, as we return to the present in Dr. Fell's study.)

DR. FELL: That can't be the end of your story, Mr. Pendleton. Did the ghostly visitor arrive?

PENDLETON: I don't know. I ran out of there and spent the night at a hotel. Today I got in touch with the telephone people. They told me the phone was disconnected yesterday morning.

DR. FELL: Are you sure it was Mary Ellen's voice you heard?

PENDLETON: Yes, and I know she is dead. I couldn't find her aunt in Kensal. I was told she had moved. But I found the doctor who treated Mary Ellen. She died from . . . starvation. She called herself Mrs. Kimball.

DR. FELL: Why did she call herself Mrs. Kimball?

90

PENDLETON *(quickly):* I don't know.

DR. FELL: Mr. Pendleton, perhaps I can help you. You must tell me the truth.

PENDLETON: I've been through enough already. I won't be cross-examined. I've already spoken about this with a man at Scotland Yard, Inspector Hadley.

DR. FELL: What did Hadley say?

PENDLETON: He said you could help me, but I can see that you won't. Good night.

(We hear his footsteps leaving. A door opens and closes.)

DR. FELL *(calling):* Hoskins!

(The door opens.)

HOSKINS: Yes, sir?

DR. FELL: Bring me my coat.

HOSKINS: You're not going out, are you, sir?

DR. FELL: Mr. Pendleton may be in real danger at home tonight.

HOSKINS: Let me call Inspector Hadley and have him meet you there.

DR. FELL: No, we don't want the police there.

HOSKINS: Why not — if that man is in danger?

DR. FELL: Never mind. Just wait till he's gone, and then get me a taxi.

(Music comes up and fades out. Then we hear a taxi pull up and stop. The taxi door opens.)

DR. FELL: Thank you, driver.

(The taxi door closes. The taxi drives off.)

DR. FELL: So this is Mr. Pendleton's house. *(We hear his footsteps start, then stop.)* Who's that standing by the gate?

HADLEY: It's Hadley, Fell. Hoskins sent for me. He said it was urgent.

DR. FELL: So, he's disobeyed me again! Well, did Pendleton get home safely tonight?

HADLEY: I don't know. I just got here. There's a light on in the library.

DR. FELL: And the door from the library to the garden is open.

PAMELA'S VOICE *(from nearby):* Oh! Who's there?

HADLEY *(surprised):* I beg your pardon, miss. It's so dark that I didn't see you.

PAMELA: That's all right. Will you let me through the gate, please? I want to see Mr. Pendleton. I'm Pamela Bennett, his secretary.

DR. FELL: I am Dr. Gideon Fell. This is Inspector Hadley from Scotland Yard.

PAMELA: I am here because Mrs. Tancred phoned the office today. She's Mr. Pendleton's housekeeper. She said Mr. Pendleton rushed out last night and hasn't been back since. He wasn't at the office today. Is he all right?

DR. FELL: I fear he isn't.

HADLEY: What do you think is wrong? Look at this place. It's as peaceful as a grave. *(A woman screams in the distance.)* What was that?

PAMELA: Look! It's Mrs. Tancred! She's coming out into the garden.

(We hear footsteps running toward them.)

MRS. TANCRED *(frightened):* Is that you, Miss Bennett?

PAMELA: Yes, Mrs. Tancred. What is the matter?

MRS. TANCRED: Mr. Pendleton has been murdered! He's lying on the floor of the library with the telephone beside him. His face is an awful color. I don't think he's breathing.

HADLEY: But there hasn't been a sound from the house.

MRS. TANCRED: Clay soil has been tracked across the floor of the library. The tracks go from the garden door to where he's lying. There are wet clay marks on Mr. Pendleton himself. It looks as if somebody covered with clay tried to hold him.

(Music comes up and fades out. A door opens.)

DR. FELL: So this is Mr. Pendleton's library.

PAMELA: Is he dead, Dr. Fell?

DR. FELL: No, Miss Bennett. He's on the way to the hospital. He's had a bad heart attack, but I'm afraid he'll pull through.

PAMELA (surprised): You're *afraid* he'll pull through?

(The wind blows. The open door to the garden slams against the house.)

DR. FELL: Don't be frightened. That was only the door to the garden being blown against the house.

PAMELA: I'm *not* frightened. What do you mean by you're *afraid* he'll pull through?

DR. FELL: Someone has been trying to scare that man out of his wits. Don't you see what happened?

PAMELA: No, I don't.

DR. FELL: As Pendleton sat here in the dim light, a ghostly figure appeared at the garden door. It wore a veil, and it walked toward him, tracking in clay. It stretched out its arms to him like this. Then —

PAMELA: Dr. Fell, please keep away from me!

DR. FELL: Forgive me. I got carried away. Would you care to hear how the whole trick worked?

PAMELA: Trick? What trick?

DR. FELL: If you asked to have your phone disconnected, they would do it at the central office. They wouldn't send someone over to yank out the wires.

PAMELA: Wasn't Mrs. Tancred telling the truth?

DR. FELL: Yes, but the man who came to disconnect the phone wasn't from the phone company. He took away the real phone and left a fake one in its place. He put a tiny microphone under this desk. It can pick up every word that is said on the phone. Do you follow me?

PAMELA: I think so.

DR. FELL: Hidden wires go from the microphone to the next room. The fake phone holds a radio receiver. So someone in the next room can talk to the person using the phone. *(Pause.)* One of two things happened tonight. Either Pendleton called Kensal 1-9-3-3, or someone pretended to call *him* from that number.

PAMELA *(tensely):* Then that "someone" must live in this house.

DR. FELL: Not necessarily. *(Pause.)* Let's be honest, Miss Bennett. Why did you try to scare your father to death? Pendleton is your father, isn't he? And Mary Ellen Kimball was your mother.

PAMELA *(through her teeth):* I do not like you, Dr. Fell.

DR. FELL *(cheerfully):* I, on the other hand, admire you a great deal. I figured you were behind this when I heard that your fiancé is a radio technician.

PAMELA: Frank set up the fake phone, but he thought it was only a joke. He's not guilty.

DR. FELL: Mary Ellen Kimball called herself "Kimball," because your father didn't want her to be known as "Mrs. Pendleton." You called yourself "Bennett" when you went to work for your father. *You* led him to the wrong gate in the cemetery. *You* put that phone number in his mind. *You* stole the key to his house. You needed it to come in here. Then you pretended to be a telephone operator and then your mother on the phone.

PAMELA (fiercely): Yes, because he killed her! He didn't use a knife or a bullet, but he broke her heart and left her to starve.

DR. FELL: Did he know about you?

PAMELA: He knew that his child would soon be born, but he never did anything about it. I'm glad I've torn his rotten life to pieces! *(She begins to cry.)* Call in Inspector Hadley. Have me arrested.

DR. FELL: You don't think I'm going to tell Hadley, do you?

PAMELA: Isn't that why he's here?

DR. FELL: No. I wanted to keep the police away from here tonight.

PAMELA: But they'll find out what happened. Look at those clay tracks on the floor.

DR. FELL: They can't be identified. They're only smudges. Pendleton could have made them himself.

PAMELA: What are you talking about?

DR. FELL: If you ask me, Pendleton kept going to the garden door, looking for a ghost. He finally went outside, then tracked in clay from the garden. He had a heart attack when he heard an imaginary noise.

PAMELA: But there won't be any clay on his shoes.

DR. FELL: Yes, there will. He didn't come home last night. His shoes will still have clay on them — from Kensal Cemetery.

HADLEY *(from a distance):* Dr. Fell? Where are you?

DR. FELL: There's Hadley now. Wipe away your tears. You've come through the rest of this with a poker face. So keep your head up. And keep repeating, "I do not like you, Dr. Fell."
(We hear footsteps approaching.)

HADLEY: Fell, there's been no crime committed here. Pendleton's own shoes have clay on them.

DR. FELL: Miss Bennett, what were you saying?

PAMELA *(almost crying):* Nothing! Nothing at all! *(Pause.)* I think I like you, Dr. Fell.
(Music comes up.)

THE END

CHECKING THE FACTS

1. Why did George Pendleton leave his wife Mary Ellen many years ago?
2. How did Mary Ellen die?
3. When this play was written, phone numbers began with letters. How does Pendleton get the idea that Kensal 1-9-3-3 is Mary Ellen's phone number?
4. How do Pamela and her fiancé set up the fake phone conversation between George Pendleton and Mary Ellen?

INTERPRETING THE PLAY

1. When Pendleton first meets Dr. Fell, why does he have clay soil on his shoes? How does this detail help clear Pamela of suspicion at the end?
2. Pendleton tells Pamela, "Mary Ellen always said she'd come back if I called her." What did Mary Ellen mean? How — and why — does Pamela twist this promise to get back at Pendleton?
3. Describe what probably happened to cause Pendleton's heart attack. What does Inspector Hadley assume happened instead?

WRITING

Suppose you are Inspector Hadley. Write a brief report about what you think happened to George Pendleton just before he was found on the floor of his library.

SUCH INTERESTING

NEIGHBORS

a play based on the story by Jack Finney

CHARACTERS

NELL LEWIS, a young woman
AL LEWIS, her husband
TED HELLENBEK, a young man
ANN HELLENBEK, his wife

> *Nell Lewis is running a vacuum cleaner in her living room. She stops by a window and stares outside. Then she switches off the vacuum cleaner.*

NELL: Here they are, Al! The new neighbors have just arrived!

> *(Her husband, Al, enters from the kitchen. He joins Nell by the window.)*

AL: There are just two of them—no kids.

NELL: They're young.

AL: Yes. They look about our age.

NELL: They must have just gotten married.

AL: Why?

NELL: Their clothes are brand-new. Even their shoes are new. So is their luggage.

AL: Yeah, maybe you're right. I'll bet they're from a foreign country.

NELL: Why do you think so?

AL: The man is having trouble figuring out what to pay the cab driver. It looks as though our money is not familiar to him.

NELL: We should go over and welcome them.

AL: That's a good idea.

> *(A moving van is parked in front of the house next door. Movers are unloading furniture. It is all brand-new. Al and Nell walk across the yard and up onto the porch. The front door is open. Inside, Ann and Ted Hellenbek are unpacking a box of dishes. The dishes are wrapped in newspapers. Ted smooths out a page and looks at it. Then he turns to Ann.)*

TED: Look, honey, here's a picture of Richard Nixon.

ANN (*looking over his shoulder*): Let's see now. Wasn't he the President before Gerald Ford?

TED: No, Ford came *after* Nixon.

ANN: I think you're wrong, dear. It was Nixon, then Ford, then—(*She stops when she sees Al and Nell standing in the doorway.*)

AL: Hi. I'm Al Lewis from next door. This is my wife, Nell. We thought we could give you a hand.

TED: I'm glad to know you. I'm Ted Hellenbek.

ANN: And I'm Ann Hellenbek.

NELL: I'm pleased to meet you. We saw you drive up in the cab. You're new to this area, aren't you?

TED: Not really. We were both born here in California. We've lived here nearly all our lives.

AL: Did you just get married?

TED (*worried*): No. We've been married for three years. Why?

AL: We were just wondering. We noticed that all of your furniture is new.

TED: Oh. Well . . . we were living in South America for a while.

ANN (*quickly*): Yes, that's right.

TED: When we decided to move back here, we sold everything. It was easier than moving it all. So we had to buy new stuff when we got here.

AL: That makes sense.

TED (*relieved*): Sure it does.

NELL: Can we help you unpack?

ANN: That's very nice of you. Would you finish this box of dishes? I want to put these pillows and sheets in the bedroom.

NELL: Sure. Go right ahead.

(*Ann picks up a pile of sheets and pillows and walks toward the bedroom. The bedroom door is closed, but Ann walks straight into it. She falls down, and Ted hurries over and helps her up.*)

TED: Be careful, honey. You'll have to learn that doors won't open by themselves. *(He laughs nervously, as though he has made a joke.)*

(Ann looks embarrassed and goes into the bedroom. Ted and Al start unpacking a box of books.)

AL: I see you have the new book by Walter Braden. I just read a review of it. The review said the book isn't very good.

TED: I know, and yet it's a great book. People today think of Braden's books as second-rate. But in 140 years, this novel will be considered a great work of art.

AL *(surprised and suspicious):* How do you know?

TED *(embarrassed):* I was just making a guess.

(Ann walks back in, carrying a pink dustcloth.)

ANN: I'd better dust off those shelves before you put the books on them. *(She dusts the shelves. Now the dustcloth is covered with streaks of dirt. She leans out a window and shakes the cloth once. The cloth is now completely clean again.)*

NELL: Where in the world did you get that wonderful dustcloth?

ANN: Why, it's just an old rag from one of Ted's suits.

AL *(to Ted):* Do you really wear pink suits?

NELL: I never saw a dustcloth that would shake out perfectly clean. I wish mine would.

ANN *(blushing):* Well, I. . . .

TED *(quickly):* The fact is, that's a special cloth. It's an invention of mine. I'm an inventor, you see.

AL: Really?

TED: Yes. I haven't gotten a patent for the dustcloth yet, though. So it's still a secret.

NELL: Don't worry. We won't tell anyone about it.

AL: What else have you invented?

TED: Have you ever seen anything like this before? *(He tosses a thin wire clip to Al.)*

AL: What is it?

TED: I call it the Safe-T-Clip. You use it the way you'd use a safety pin. Only there's no danger of sticking yourself with a sharp point. Look. *(He slides the clip onto Al's shirt collar.)* Now try to take it off.

(Al pulls hard at his collar, but he can't take off the clip.)

AL: I give up. How do you open it?

(Ted shows him how to press the wire at a certain place. The clip slides right off.)

AL: That's amazing. How did you ever think it up?

TED: It was easy.

ANN: Ted, I don't like to interrupt you. But would you set up the stereo?

TED: I'll try.

(Ted doesn't seem to know much about a stereo. He tries to plug wires into the wrong places. He can't figure out how to attach the different parts together. Al and Nell are surprised that an inventor doesn't know more about this equipment.)

(Later, Nell and Al are back home, discussing their new neighbors.)

NELL: They seem like nice people. I bet they'll be good neighbors.

AL: I think so, too. But there's something odd about them.

NELL: In what way?

AL: I'm not sure. Maybe it's because he's an inventor and they used to live in South America. They're not like everybody else.

NELL: That's what I like about them. They're such interesting people. *(Pause.)* But I know what you mean. It's nothing big, but there's something about them that doesn't quite fit together.

(Several weeks pass. The two couples become good friends. One evening, Nell and Al are sitting on their porch after supper. Nell is knitting, and Al is reading a science-fiction magazine. Ann and Ted drop by.)

ANN: Hi. It's a nice evening, isn't it?

NELL: It sure is. Have a seat.

(Ann and Ted sit down.)

TED: What are you reading, Al?

AL: It's a science-fiction magazine. Do you ever read this kind of stuff? *(He hands the magazine to Ted.)*

TED *(looking through it):* This is very interesting.

AL: Some of the stories are good. There's one in there about a man of the future who escapes back to our time. But the secret police of the future follow him and take him back.

TED: I'd like to read that. *(Pause.)* I wrote a science-fiction story once. It's about the world of the future, and—

ANN *(nervously):* What are you talking about, Ted?

TED: Ann is always afraid I'll bore people with my ideas.

ANN: Well, this one is silly.

NELL *(calming her down):* I know what you mean about science-fiction stories. I can't understand why Al reads that sort of thing.

AL: Don't worry. It's harmless. Go on, Ted.

TED: Actually, I wrote this story with a friend of mine. He was a printer, so we printed some copies of the story. Would you like to see one?

AL: Sure.

TED: I'll be right back. *(He goes over to his house.)*

ANN *(worried):* I don't know where Ted gets his crazy ideas.

NELL: Well, he *is* an inventor. Unusual ideas are his business.

ANN: But I don't like it when he starts all this talk about the future. He's just making it all up, you know.

NELL: Of course. It's just science fiction.
(Ted returns, carrying a long, narrow strip of paper. He hands it to Al.)

AL: This paper feels strange.

TED: Well, people won't go out and buy magazines in the future. They will receive stories and articles on their home computers. And the computers will print the words on special paper. You have in your hands a magazine of the future. I mean, it's what my friend and I imagined a magazine of the future would be like.

AL *(reading aloud):* "Scientists are worried about the TT fad."

NELL: What's "TT" ?

TED: Time Travel. People of the future will have machines that will let them travel through time. You could go to any period in history and stay as long as you like.

AL: That sounds like fun.

TED: Sure, it *sounds* great, unless you know more about the world of the future. Imagine it. The human race has built powerful, deadly weapons. Everyone lives in fear of being blown up at any second.

NELL: That's no different from the world today.

TED: Oh, but it is! It's peaceful today compared to what it *will* be like. Your weapons—I mean, *our* weapons—are not yet highly developed. We have only atomic and hydrogen bombs.

ANN: I think it's time for you to stop, Ted.

AL: No. I want to hear this.

TED: Life will barely be worth living. Taxes and prices will be sky-high. The air, the soil, and the water will be polluted. There will be crime everywhere. And hanging over everything will be the fear of sudden death and destruction.

ANN *(bitterly)*: It's not the way human beings were meant to live.

TED: Then they discover Time Travel. It's the only way to escape. People take their vacations in other periods of time. They can enjoy clean beaches and beautiful forests back in the year 1000. Or they can visit their favorite time in history.

ANN: But it doesn't always turn out right.

TED: That's true. Sometimes it's not safe. In this story we made up, a man in Kansas arrives home bleeding to death from arrow wounds. He got caught in the middle of a battle. In Florida, a whole family disappears. Their TT set is still on, but they are never seen again. In Chicago, a man returns from a week in France in the Middle Ages. Two days

106

later, he dies of the plague. Everyone is afraid that the disease will spread, although it doesn't.

NELL: But wouldn't people learn to be more careful?

TED: Yes. Like anything new, Time Travel takes practice. The important thing is that people can escape. They can go back to simpler times, to times when life was worth living. So everybody starts using Time Travel.

AL: How does the story end?

TED: More and more people find a wonderful place in the past. Then they ask themselves, "Why not stay here? Why return?" And people just stop going back home.

NELL: But if people don't go back, what happens to the world?

TED: Soon nearly everyone has gone. The world is left to a handful of people who *like* wars. But there is no one left to fight their wars with them. So they give up and join their families and friends in earlier times, too.

AL: Then the planet would be deserted.

TED: That's right. That's how the world ends.

NELL: I must admit that it's an interesting story. But there are a few holes in it.

TED: Like what?

NELL: Wouldn't people in those earlier times notice that a lot of new people were moving in?

TED: I don't think so. A few billion people scatter themselves through thousands of years, all over the world. At any one time or place, they wouldn't be noticed.

AL: I guess not. But wouldn't these people of the future start making modern inventions in those earlier times?

TED: I doubt it. Suppose you went back 100 years in time. Could you make a television set?

AL: No. I don't know how it works.

TED: Right. But suppose you *did* know how it works. You might not be able to find the right materials to build one. Even if you could, what would happen? You would show it to people, and they would think you were crazy. They'd lock you up. The best thing you could do would be to show them one or two very simple things.

AL *(quietly):* Like the Safe-T-Clip?

108

TED: Yes, something like that. You see, Al, you'd have to take your place in the world as you found it.

NELL: But wouldn't you ever miss the world you had grown up in?

ANN *(sadly):* Yes. You would also get lonely for old friends. But what could you go back to? There's nothing left but an empty earth of wind, rain, and rusting weapons.

(A year later, Nell and Al are eating supper at home alone.)

NELL: I miss Ann and Ted. I wish they hadn't moved to New Jersey.

AL: Well, you can't blame them. Some of their old friends were about to move there. Ted and Ann wanted to be there to welcome them.

NELL: I know, but I wish they still lived next door. The new neighbors are perfectly nice people. But after the Hellenbeks, they're kind of dull.

THE END

CHECKING THE FACTS

1. When Ann and Ted first appear, why does Nell think they have just gotten married? Why does Al think they are from a foreign country?
2. What surprising thing does Ann's dustcloth do? What surprising thing does Ted's Safe-T-Clip do?
3. Why are Al and Nell surprised when Ted can't set up the stereo?
4. What is "TT" ? What does it allow people to do?
5. Why do Nell and Al miss Ted and Ann at the end?

INTERPRETING THE PLAY

1. Why do you think Ann walks into a closed door?
2. Why does Ted seem to know that a relatively unknown book will be considered a great work of art within 140 years?
3. Why do you think Ted tells Al and Nell that he is an inventor?
4. Why do you think Ted is so eager to tell Al and Nell about the "science-fiction story" he has written? Why doesn't Ann seem to want Ted to talk about it?

WRITING

Think of a place in the past or the future that might be exciting to visit. Write a "time travel" ad for visiting it. Write the ad as if it were to be announced on the radio.

THE RED-HEADED LEAGUE

a Sherlock Holmes mystery by Sir Arthur Conan Doyle

CHARACTERS

SHERLOCK HOLMES, the famous English detective
DR. JOHN WATSON, his friend and assistant
JABEZ WILSON, owner of a pawnshop
VINCENT SPAULDING, a clerk in the pawnshop
DUNCAN ROSS, a member of the Red-Headed League
PETER JONES, a Scotland Yard detective
REGINALD MERRYWEATHER, a bank president
JOHN CLAY, a criminal whose identity will be revealed
    later

SCENE ONE

*It is a Saturday morning in the summer of 1890. Dr.
Watson enters Sherlock Holmes's sitting room. Holmes
is there talking with a man who has bright red hair.*

HOLMES: Watson, you could not have come at a better
    time.

WATSON: You seem to be busy. I can wait outside.

HOLMES: Not at all. *(He turns to the man with the red
    hair.)* Dr. Watson has helped me in many of my
    cases, Mr. Wilson. I have no doubt he will be help-
    ful in yours.

WILSON: How do you do?

WATSON: How do you do, sir?

HOLMES: Watson, I know you share my love of the
    unusual. Mr. Wilson has started to tell me one of
    the strangest stories I've ever heard. Mr. Wilson,
    will you be kind enough to begin your story again?

WILSON: Of course.

HOLMES: I am sure, Watson, you can tell that Mr. Wil-
    son has been in China.

WATSON *(puzzled):* Well. . . .

HOLMES: And you can see that he has been doing a
    lot of writing.

WILSON *(amazed):* How did you know that?

HOLMES: The cuff on your right sleeve is very shiny. Your left sleeve has a smooth patch at the elbow, where you rest it on a desk. It is clear that you've been writing a lot with your right hand, while leaning on your left elbow.

WILSON: That's true. But how did you know that I've been in China?

HOLMES: There is a tattoo of a fish above your wrist. I have made a study of tattoos. Only in China are the fish scales colored pink, as they are in your tattoo.

WILSON *(laughing):* I thought at first you had done something very clever. But I see now that it was really very simple.

HOLMES: Perhaps, Watson, I should not give away my ways of drawing conclusions. I might lose my reputation as a genius. Now, Mr. Wilson, will you read us the newspaper ad that led to your adventure?

WILSON *(reading a newspaper ad aloud):* "There is a position open in the Red-Headed League. According to the will of the late Elmer Hopkins, of the U.S.A., a League member will be paid a high salary for doing easy work. Red-headed men over the age of 21 may apply. See Duncan Ross at 7 Pope's Court, Monday at 11:00 a.m."

WATSON: What on earth does this mean?

HOLMES: Please note the paper and the date, Watson.

WATSON *(looking at the ad):* It is from *The Morning Chronicle,* April 27, 1890. That was two months ago.

HOLMES: Now, Mr. Wilson, tell us your story.

WILSON: I own a pawnshop on Coburg Square. It's a small business, and I don't make much money. In fact, I pay my assistant only half the usual salary. He was willing to take the job in order to learn the business.

HOLMES: What is this young fellow's name?

WILSON: His name is Vincent Spaulding, and he isn't very young. He does his job well, but he has one fault. He spends too much time on his hobby, photography. He always seems to be down in the cellar, developing his pictures.

WATSON: He doesn't sound very helpful.

WILSON: Oh, but he is. It was Spaulding who showed me this newspaper ad two months ago. . . .

SCENE TWO

The scene is Wilson's pawnshop, two months earlier. Spaulding enters.

SPAULDING: Mr. Wilson, I wish I had red hair.

WILSON: Why?

SPAULDING (*handing him the ad*): There's another opening in the Red-Headed League.

WILSON: What is that?

SPAULDING: Haven't you ever heard of it? Why, *you* could apply for the job, with hair that color. You get paid well for doing very little work. You could handle that job—and still run this shop.

WILSON: I certainly could use the money. Tell me about this Red-Headed League.

SPAULDING: It was started by an American millionaire who was a bit odd. He was red-headed. When he died, he left his fortune to help red-headed men live an easy life.

WILSON: I'm sure that thousands of men will apply for the job opening.

SPAULDING: No. You have to live in London. Elmer Hopkins lived in London for a while, and he wanted to do something good for the city. Also, your hair cannot be light red or dark red. It must be as bright red as yours.

WILSON: Spaulding, let's close up the shop for an hour or so. We're going to visit the office of the Red-Headed League.

114

SCENE THREE

Wilson and Spaulding join a line of red-headed men out-side a small office. The line moves forward as the men ahead of them enter the office, one by one, then quickly come out again.

WILSON: Did all these men see the ad?

SPAULDING: Oh, yes. The League is very well-known.

WILSON: I don't have a chance of getting the job.

SPAULDING: You do, sir. There aren't many men here with hair as bright as yours.

(Now they are at the open door of the office. Duncan Ross, a man with bright red hair, is sitting at a desk. Another red-headed man is standing before him.)

ROSS *(to the red-headed man)*: I'm sorry, sir. Your hair is a bit too orange for us. *(The man leaves.)* Next!

SPAULDING *(leading Wilson forward)*: This is Mr. Jabez Wilson. He is willing to join the League.

ROSS: Well, he has a very fine head of red hair. *(He stands up and walks around Wilson, looking at his head. Suddenly he pulls Wilson's hair.)*

WILSON *(surprised)*: Ow!

ROSS: Good. That hair is real. We have to be careful. We've been tricked twice by wigs and once by boot polish. *(He shouts out the doorway.)* You men may all go home now! The job has been filled! *(He turns to Wilson.)* My name is Duncan Ross. I'm part of the League. When can you start working for us?

WILSON: Well, I have a business of my own already.

SPAULDING: Never mind that, Mr. Wilson. I'll be able to look after the shop.

ROSS: The hours here are from 10:00 in the morning until 2:00 in the afternoon.

WILSON: That's fine. Most of my business takes place late in the afternoon or early in the evening. Spaulding can handle anything that turns up in the morning. What is the work I'm to do?

ROSS: It is very simple, but you must stay in this office the whole time. If you leave, you lose the job. The will of Mr. Hopkins states that very clearly. No excuse will be accepted, not even sickness.

WILSON: What is the work?

ROSS: You copy an encyclopedia. Here is the first volume. *(He hands a volume to Wilson.)* You bring your own ink, pens, and paper. We provide this desk and chair. Can you start tomorrow?

WILSON: Yes.

ROSS: Then let me congratulate you. You are lucky to be a member of the Red-Headed League.

SCENE FOUR

The scene is Holmes's sitting room once again. Wilson continues to tell his story to Holmes and Watson.

WILSON: I was sure the whole thing was a prank. I couldn't believe that anyone would pay a high salary for copying an encyclopedia. But I decided to go through with it. To my surprise, everything seemed to be in order.

HOLMES: Were you paid?

WILSON: Yes.

HOLMES: Was Mr. Ross always there?

WILSON: He dropped by for the first few days. Then I saw less and less of him. But I never dared to leave the office. I never knew when he might appear. If he found I wasn't there, I would lose the job.

WATSON: How long did this go on?

WILSON: For eight weeks. I wrote about abbots and archery and armor. Then, suddenly, it all came to an end.

HOLMES: To an end?

WILSON: Yes, sir. At 10:00 this morning, I went to the office as usual, but the door was locked. This card was tacked on the door. *(He hands a card to Holmes.)* You can read it for yourself.

HOLMES *(reading aloud):* "The Red-Headed League no longer exists." What did you do after you found this card?

WILSON: I went to the landlord. He said he had never heard of the Red-Headed League or of Mr. Duncan Ross. But he had rented the office to a red-headed man named William Morris. Mr. Morris, he said, moved out yesterday.

HOLMES: Did he give you Mr. Morris' new address?

WILSON: Yes, and I went there. No one there had heard of either William Morris or Duncan Ross.

WATSON: What did you do then?

WILSON: I went back to my shop and talked to Spaulding. He said there was nothing I could do but wait to see if Mr. Ross would write me a letter. But I didn't want to lose a job like that without a struggle. I had heard that you, Mr. Holmes, give advice to poor people who need help. So here I am.

HOLMES: You were wise to come here. I shall be happy to look into your case. This might be more serious than it seems at first sight.

WILSON: Of course it's serious! I've lost a good job. I want to know more about this Red-Headed League. Why did they play this prank upon me? Or wasn't it a prank?

HOLMES: We shall try to clear up these questions. First, tell me more about Spaulding. How long had he worked for you before he showed you the newspaper ad?

WILSON: About a month.

HOLMES: Before you hired him, did anyone else apply for the job?

WILSON: Yes. There were several people.

HOLMES: Why did you pick Spaulding?

WILSON: He was willing to accept half the usual salary.

HOLMES: What does he look like?

WILSON: He is small and stout and about 30 years old. He has a white mark on his forehead from some acid.

HOLMES: I thought so! Are his ears pierced for earrings?

WILSON: Yes. He said a gypsy pierced them for him when he was a boy.

HOLMES: Does he still work for you?

WILSON: Yes, sir.

HOLMES: That will do for now, Mr. Wilson. I will be happy to give you my opinion in two days.

WILSON: Thank you, Mr. Holmes. Good day, Dr. Watson. *(He leaves.)*

HOLMES: Well, Watson, what do you make of all this?

WATSON: I make nothing of it. It is a mysterious business. What are you going to do about it?

HOLMES: I'm going to smoke my pipe and think. Please do not disturb me for an hour. At the end of that time, we shall go to Coburg Square.

SCENE FIVE

An hour later, Holmes and Watson are outside Wilson's pawnshop on Coburg Square. Holmes knocks on the door, and Spaulding opens it.

SPAULDING: May I help you?

HOLMES: Can you tell me how to get to Fleet Street from here?

SPAULDING: Take the third right and the fourth left. *(He goes back into the shop.)*

HOLMES: Watson, Spaulding is the fourth smartest man in London. He is also one of the most daring. I have heard of him before.

WATSON: You seem to think he matters a great deal in this mystery. I suppose you asked for directions so you could get a look at him.

HOLMES: No, not at *him*. I wanted to see the knees of his trousers.

WATSON: What did you see?

HOLMES: What I expected to see. Now, Watson, we must study the buildings on this street. I wish to remember the order. On the corner is a tobacco shop. Next is a newspaper shop. Then there is Wilson's pawnshop. Next to that is the Coburg branch of the Bank of London. Then there is a restaurant. Finally, there is a tailor's shop.

WATSON: Why is the order of the buildings important?

HOLMES: A serious crime has been planned. I believe we still have time to stop it. I shall need your help tonight.

WATSON: At what time will you need me?

HOLMES: At 10:00 at my place. There may be some danger, so bring your army revolver.

SCENE SIX

At 10:00 that night, Watson enters Holmes's sitting room. Holmes is talking with two men.

HOLMES: Ah, Watson, you know Peter Jones of Scotland Yard. Let me introduce you to Reginald Merryweather. He is the president of a branch of the Bank of London.

WATSON: How do you do, sir?

JONES: Well, Watson, your friend Holmes is a wonderful man for starting a chase.

MERRYWEATHER *(frowning):* I hope that a wild goose is not at the end of it.

JONES: You may trust Mr. Holmes. His ways of solving mysteries are a little unusual. But now and then he does a better job than our police force.

MERRYWEATHER: All right, but I am missing my Saturday night poker game. It is the first Saturday night in 27 years that I have not played poker.

HOLMES: Mr. Merryweather, you will play for higher stakes tonight than you have ever done before. And the game will be more exciting. The prize for you is a huge amount of money. The prize for you, Mr. Jones, is John Clay.

MERRYWEATHER: Who is John Clay?

JONES: He is a murderer, thief, and forger. I would rather arrest him than any other criminal in London. He's the grandson of a duke. His brain is as swift as his fingers. We find signs of his evil work everywhere, but we've never found the man himself. I've been on his track for years.

HOLMES: I hope that I may be able to introduce him to you tonight. Now, Mr. Merryweather, let us go to your bank on Coburg Square.

SCENE SEVEN

The four men are now in the cellar of Mr. Merryweather's bank. Mr. Merryweather is carrying a lantern. The cellar is filled with crates.

HOLMES *(looking at the ceiling):* It doesn't look as if anyone could break in from above.

MERRYWEATHER: Nor could anyone break in from below. *(He hits the stone floor with his walking stick.)* Why, it sounds hollow!

HOLMES *(taking the lantern from him):* I must ask you to be more quiet. Please sit on one of those crates and don't interfere. *(He gets down on his knees, and examines the stone floor.)*

WATSON: What are you doing, Holmes?

HOLMES: I am checking these stones. *(He stands up.)* Well, we must wait until Mr. Wilson goes to bed.

JONES: What do you mean?

HOLMES: Mr. Wilson owns the pawnshop next door. He lives above the shop. As soon as he is asleep, John Clay and his men will make their move. Mr. Merryweather can explain why John Clay would be interested in this cellar.

MERRYWEATHER *(whispering):* It's the shipment of gold from France. We have thousands of pounds worth of gold here. It's in these crates. Why, the crate I'm sitting on holds a fortune. We heard that an attempt might be made to steal it.

HOLMES: I believe that this will happen soon. Mr. Merryweather, I must cover the lantern.

MERRYWEATHER: Must we sit in the dark?

HOLMES: I'm afraid so. These are daring men. They will harm us if we are not careful. I shall stand behind this crate. The rest of you hide behind those crates. When I flash the light upon the criminals, close in quickly. If they fire, fire back.
(Silence.)

MERRYWEATHER: This waiting could drive me mad.

HOLMES: Control yourself, Merryweather. Jones, I hope you did what I asked you to do.

JONES: Yes. Two officers are at the front door of the pawnshop.

HOLMES: Good. That is the only way they could escape.

WATSON *(quietly)*: Look. Some light is shining between the stones in the floor.

HOLMES *(calmly)*: I see it. Be ready.

(Suddenly a large stone is pushed up from the floor. Then two men climb up through the hole and into the cellar. One has red hair.)

CLAY *(to the red-headed man)*: It's all clear. *(Holmes uncovers the lantern and grabs Clay.)* Jump, Archie!

(The red-headed man jumps down through the hole in the floor. Jones grabs his jacket, but the cloth rips.)

WATSON: Holmes, watch out for Clay's gun!

HOLMES *(knocking the gun out of Clay's hand)*: It's no use, John Clay.

CLAY: So I see. At least my pal got away.

HOLMES: I'm afraid not. Two police officers are waiting for him at the door to the pawnshop.

CLAY: You seem to have handled everything very well. I must compliment you.

HOLMES: And I compliment *you*. Your red-headed idea was very clever.

JONES: Clay, you and your partner are coming to the police station. Now, hold out your hands for these. *(He puts handcuffs on Clay.)*

CLAY: Be careful with your filthy hands. You may not be aware that I have royal blood in my veins. Have the goodness to say "please" and "sir" when you speak to me.

JONES: All right. Would you please, sir, march upstairs?

CLAY *(calmly):* That is better. *(He bows to the others, then walks off with Jones.)*

MERRYWEATHER: Mr. Holmes, I don't know how my bank can repay you.

HOLMES: I have had several scores to settle with Mr. John Clay. I shall expect the bank to pay my expenses in this case. Otherwise, I have already been well paid by having this adventure.

SCENE EIGHT

Later, Holmes and Watson discuss the case in Holmes's sitting room.

HOLMES: Why was the ad placed in the newspaper? And why was Mr. Wilson hired to copy an encyclopedia? It was to get him out of the way for four hours every day. Clay dreamed up the idea of the Red-Headed League because his partner and Wilson both have bright red hair.

WATSON: So the Red-Headed League never existed.

HOLMES: Exactly. Clay, calling himself Vincent Spaulding, got himself hired by Wilson. We heard that he was working for Wilson for half the usual salary. I knew then that he had a strong reason for taking that job.

WATSON: But how could you guess what that was?

HOLMES: According to Wilson, photography was Spaulding's hobby. He spent many hours in the cellar. I figured he was digging a tunnel to another building. So I went to the pawnshop to ask for some directions.

WATSON: You said you wanted to get a look at Spaulding's—I mean Clay's trousers.

HOLMES: Right. I saw that the knees of his trousers were worn and dirty. That meant hours of digging. But what was he digging for? We saw that the Bank of London is next to Wilson's shop. That was the answer.

WATSON: How could you tell that they would break in tonight?

HOLMES: Well, they closed the Red-Headed League office. That was a sign that they no longer needed Mr. Wilson out of the way. In other words, they had finished their tunnel. Saturday would be the best day to steal the gold. The bank would be closed, and they would have two days to escape.

The theft would not be discovered until Monday.

WATSON: You thought it all out perfectly!

HOLMES: Oh, these little problems keep me from being bored. And this case gave me the added satisfaction of seeing John Clay arrested. Perhaps now there will be a little less evil done in London.

THE END

CHECKING THE FACTS

1. How does Mr. Wilson learn about the Red-Headed League? When he joins the League, what is his job?
2. Why does Wilson go to Sherlock Holmes for advice?
3. Wilson tells Holmes that Spaulding spends a lot of time in the cellar. What does Wilson think Spaulding is doing down there?
4. Holmes visits the pawnshop to ask Spaulding for directions. What is the real reason for this visit?

INTERPRETING THE PLAY

1. Why is Wilson paid so much to do such useless work for the Red-Headed League? Does the League really exist? Explain.
2. What does Sherlock Holmes suspect that Spaulding is doing in the cellar of Wilson's pawnshop? Why?
3. When Holmes visits the pawnshop, what does he notice about Spaulding? Why is he interested in the order of the buildings on Coburg Square?
4. How does Holmes figure out when the theft will be attempted?

WRITING

Suppose you are Dr. Watson, and you want to describe Sherlock Holmes's ability to draw important conclusions from small details. Write an explanation of how Holmes figured out that Mr. Wilson had been doing a lot of writing and had been in China.